Fishing out of Whitby

Fishing out of Whitby

John Tindale

Dalesman Books · 1987

The Dalesman Publishing Company Ltd.
Clapham, Lancaster LA2 8EB
First published 1987
© John Tindale, 1987.

ISBN: 0 85206 912 X

*In memory of Charles Tindale
whose morning's pleasure was to walk down
the pier and talk with the fishermen*

Printed by Smiths of Bradford

Contents

The author acknowledges the information obtained from books and publications by: Dora M. Walker;
H. Shaw Jeffrey; Hugh P. Kendall; J.T. Sewell – "Mediaeval Roads"; E. Keble Chatterton –
"Whales and Whaling"; Michael A. Bortoft – "The Whitby Whale Fishery"; Whitby Literary &
Philosophical Society Library; H.M. Customs and Excise; Michael Moore in "Yorkshire Life";
"Whitby Gazette" letters; T. H. English.
    He also appreciates and acknowledges personal comments and reminiscences by T. H. Ashworth;
Clem James (Chairman, North Eastern Sea Fisheries Committee); Jim Leadley (President and Chairman
of the National Fisherman's Federation); and Robert Peart.
    Photographs are the copyright of The Sutcliffe Gallery, Flowergate, Whitby; John Tindale,
14 Skinner Street, Whitby; and the Whitby Literary & Philosophical Society. The source of some older
prints and photographs has been impossible to trace.

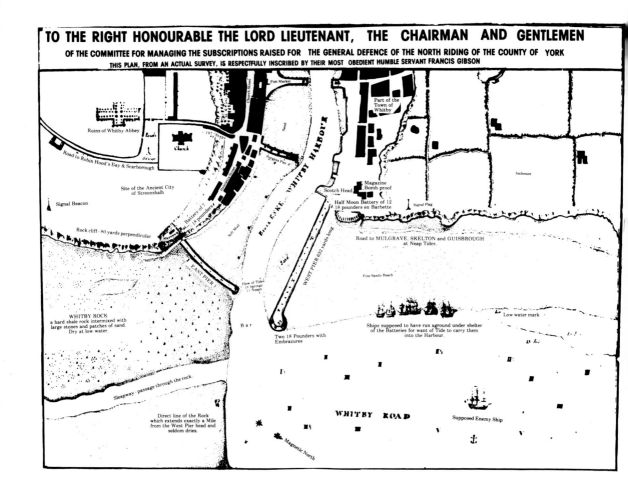

TO THE RIGHT HONOURABLE THE LORD LIEUTENANT, THE CHAIRMAN AND GENTLEMEN

OF THE COMMITTEE FOR MANAGING THE SUBSCRIPTIONS RAISED FOR THE GENERAL DEFENCE OF THE NORTH RIDING OF THE COUNTY OF YORK

THIS PLAN, FROM AN ACTUAL SURVEY, IS RESPECTFULLY INSCRIBED BY THEIR MOST OBEDIENT HUMBLE SERVANT FRANCIS GIBSON

Observations on the Town and Port of Whitby

With its Natural and Artificial Defences annexed to a plan of the Coast on the North and South sides of the harbour in 1794.

WHITBY, the principal Port in the North Riding, is, from its situation and distance from any Military Station, peculiarly liable to the insults of the Enemy by sea. It hath therefore been judged absolutely necessary since the commencement of the present War to augment and improve its Batteries, not only for the preservation of internal property, but for the safety of vessels which frequently seek for protection under its Cannon. For these reasons the Half Moon Battery was formed, which is now furnished with 12 18-pounders mounted on Barbettes from which shot may be sent with effect into every part of WHITBY ROAD.

Without this, and commanded by it, are 2 18-pounders planted on the West Pier Head, with Embrazures, likewise commanding the Road.

A Plan, which I had the honour to give in, having been adopted, a Battery was constructed on an inaccessible part of the East Cliff, 50 feet above high Water mark, mounted with 7 18-pounders which completely overlooks and commands the other two Batteries, forming a crossfire to each. So that should any vessels be chased inshore and for lack of water into the Harbour be obliged to run aground under the Half Moon, the Enemy might destroy them, while the fire from that Battery could not be directed against him but through our own Ships, for this reason the East Battery was formed, every Ball from which might explode the Enemy's Ships while, from the Elevation, no shot of his could take effect.

The Town of Whitby contains upwards of 14,000 inhabitants. Its great staple trade is Shipbuilding. Twenty-five vessels of an average Tonnage of 300 tons, being annually built, and there are seldom less than Twelve large Ships upon the Stocks. Before the sailing of the Baltic Fleet in the Spring of 1793, thirty-two large ships were detained by contrary winds whose average value was at least £60,000. Those with twelve upon the Stocks and 5 in the Dry Docks.

The Town, Ropehouses, Magazines of Pitch, Tar and Resin might (as the Harbour dries at low water) have been easily destroyed by an enterprizing Enemy, had not adequate defences been provided.

For these, and many other reasons, WHITBY has a peculiar claim upon the North Riding for support, as being the only Sea-Port in it that requires such support, Scarborough being a Royal Garrison and infintely more tenable.

The number of Shipping belonging to WHITBY is 274, employing 2610 able Seamen.

Its Imports, Coal, Timber, Hemp, Flax and Iron.

Exports 260,000 Yards of Sail Cloth chiefly for the use of the Royal Navy. 2,000 tons of Alum, 500 tons Whale Oil, 40 tons of Whale Bone, with Butter, Hams, Salmon and Salted Cod.

Francis Gibson
Whitby, September 28th 1794

(These observations were printed with the drawing of Whitby).

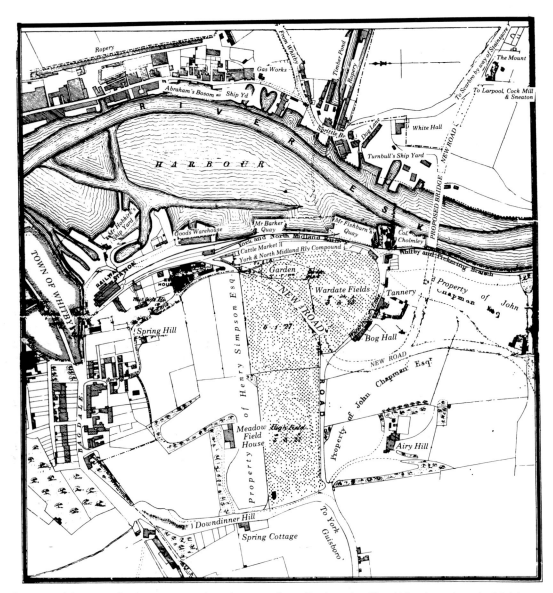

This map of the upper harbour was produced as part of an offer for sale of land (the dotted area) which is now filled with houses, the agents avowing that, despite George Hudson's development of the West Cliff hotel and residential area, there would still be a need for artisans' dwellings in the town. Fishburn's Yard where three of James Cook's ships were built, is marked, as are some other yards and dry docks, a timber pond and ropery. The date was 1853; the map shows a suggested new road and bridge across the Esk – the bridge in much the same position as the High Level bridge recently completed. The route of the suggested road which was designed to cut out steep hills for coaches and horses was not followed – but would have removed much of the present traffic congestion had it been made.

1. In the beginning . . .

Why a book about fishing at Whitby rather than one of a dozen places on the North East coast? Fishing is fishing. The excuses may be that the first written record goes back more than 1300 years, that the town became the ninth port of importance in the kingdom in the 1700s because of its shipbuilding industry, that it was a whaling centre at the end of the century, that it was the North East's centre for the herring fleets in this century and today is still a busy fishing port.

The first mention of a fishing boat putting out from Whitby is made by Bede, when the Princess Aelfleda of Whitby Abbey in 654AD set off to visit St Cuthbert further north on one of the boats used by the lay brethren of the abbey. If monks were fishermen, then there must have been others. In fact fishing must have gone on since whatever year there were people living around the mouth of the river Esk; the arrival of the Lady Hild and her mixed group of males and females to establish a monastery on the cliff top and gradually to become the rulers and administrators of the area must have regularised the fishing to produce food for all, probably to the annoyance of the sturdy and independent original residents.

Two centuries later the Danish invaders landed in the bay on one of their forays, and "swept the monastery with fire and sword, pillaging its treasures and destroying its buildings". The present ruins of stone buildings on the East Cliff are not the result of the Danish invasion – the original monastery was comprised of mud and wattle buildings around a similarly constructed central chapel, and was dedicated to Saint Peter. The present ruins are of later date, the outcome of Henry

VIII's dissolution of the monasteries. The re-building after the Danes began shortly after 1066 when William the Conqueror's retinue included rich French families who funded new monastic establishments in several parts of Yorkshire. But, to revert to the Danish era, it is recorded that a few fishermen's huts were erected among the ruins, and when the abbot of the new monastery arrived he started to collect tithes. Fish must have been a definite source of income for the abbey, and the local fishermen, who had for two hundred years been free of resident overlords, would have found the Abbot's demands very trying. The abbey buildings included a Fish House and from an inventory in 1394 – taken when a new abbot was installed – we know that it contained 120 codlings, eight lasts of herring, 300 salt fish, and three barrels of white herring. There is a report that in that same year some 30,000 herring were brought in *at one catch.*

It is reported that "a vast shoal arrived" and some foreigners were attracted who sold the fish for export – shades of things to come! Threepence in the pound was charged until complaints were made that the natives were being deprived of their food and further sales for export were forbidden.

The end of the rule of the abbots came when a new incumbent had just sworn allegiance to Thomas Cromwell on December 9th, 1538 and had the job of surrendering the abbey to the commissioners of Henry VIII a year later on December 14th, 1539. In 1550 the abbey estates were sold to the Earl of Warwick who in the following year conveyed them to Sir Richard Cholmley, where they remained until 1883 when they passed by marriage to the Strickland family, of Boynton, who are the

Whitby Abbey, on a 200 feet high cliff, was supplied with water from a well near Hawsker which is still there; water not only for domestic purposes but also to feed the pond where the Abbot kept fish for the table. A drought in the 1980s killed off the last of the pike.

Lords of the Manor to this day.

No sooner had the monastery been dissolved than Whitby became a fishing boom town with boats of thirty to forty tons navigating through a good deep harbour entrance, and seventy-four small craft operating as well. The King's Antiquary, John Leland, on his tour of the country about 1535-43, visited Whitby and described it as "a great Fischar toune" possessing "an havenet holp with a peere" (a small harbour helped by a pier). There is no known record of when Whitby first had a pier but there was a grant to the abbot from King Edward I in 1307 "for a quay newly to be constructed" and other similar grants were made in the reigns of Edward II, Henry IV and Henry VI. In 1562 every Wednesday was decreed a fish day in the Royal Navy – which would recompense in some way for the population officially leaving the Church of Rome with its decree of fish on Friday – or did the general populace take much notice in their dietary habits?

After 1539 there is a record that the piers were maintained by the king, with supplies of timber from the king's forests. By the year 1676

The east side of Whitby with St. Mary's Parish Church on the 200 feet high cliff. On the harbourside at the right of the picture is John Walker's house where Captain James Cook lived as an apprentice and which opened in 1987 as a museum with Cook memorabilia.

the harbour had silted up preventing the larger boats from working, unemployment was rife in the fishing industry and it became centred in the nearby coastal villages of Staithes, Runswick, Sandsend and Robin Hood's Bay. Whitby's fishing families were reduced to nine only. The harbour was wide open to the North Sea, with no protective piers outside of the present Scotch Head and the Burgess (Tate Hill) Pier. "Outside these the sea washed up a great abundance and rendered the entrance to the harbour extremely difficult and dangerous. No vessels of burden could go in and out,

especially with any loading in. For want of a proper place of refuge many lives were lost near the port in stormy and tempestuous weather." In 1702 Parliament passed a decree to raise funds for the building of proper piers, laying down that for nine years taxes should be payable on goods passing the port on its way from Newcastle to London "towards the repairing and rebuilding of the pieres at Whitby". For landing the coals at Whitby, sixpence per chauldron (twelve sacks), salt two shillings; for every quarter of malt, grain or corn, four pence. For all foreign goods imported into Whitby in English ships, three pence per ton. Butter one penny per firkin, dried fish and mud fish one penny per score, barrelled fish three pence per barrel. For throwing dust, ash, ballast, rubbish, stones or any other annoyance whatsoever into the harbour, forty shillings. The dues were collected by appointed men who took sixpence in the pound for their work. However, the work did not go as scheduled, the trustees mortgaged the dues up to the hilt and then had to beg Parliament for an extension until May 1723.

With the money raised the East Pier was built about two hundred yards long and this was a security to the town "as it entirely curbed the violence of the waves that till then, whenever the wind was in the north east had always flowed over the rock with a strong current right into the harbour." On the west side a staith was built and a western pier of about 200 yards which may have been theoretically correct but in practice threw a vast

quantity of sand into the Collier Hope and rendered the channel very narrow. The "utter destruction of the harbour was threatened, and not even fresh water coming down the harbour could move it", so another Parliament Act put back the duty on coal to pay for an extension of another hundred yards on the West Pier. The stone came from Aislaby quarry – three miles outside the town – on carts drawn by oxen. Some of the stones were "six tonners", and were taken by narrow Waterstead Lane down to John Bolton's wharf in the upper harbour for water transport to their destination. In R. B. Holt's *Whitby Past and Present,* there is a picturesque description of the scene when foot passengers encountered an ox wagon on its way:

> To meet one of the wagons in Waterstead Lane was a terror to nervous people. The big horns and straining eyes of the huge brutes were bad enough; but instead of keeping upright in a respectable fashion they leaned inwards and sloped their legs outwards so that your only choice was to turn back, to find a refuge in some gateway, or to scramble into a hedge and hold on by the thorn bushes till the creatures had lumbered past you.

There was another method of taking the blocks of stone from Aislaby Quarry down to the harbour which to present generations seems incredible but is proved by documents in the possession of Whitby Museum. There is an outflow in the Dock End of the upper harbour bringing water from "Bagdale Beck";

EMPRESS OF INDIA
LEITH

WHITBY, YORKSHIRE.—WITH THE RECENT IMPROVEMENTS.

Above
Whitby in the 1860s "with the recent improvements" which included the cutting of Khyber Pass from the harbourside up to the West Cliff where Hudson, the "Railway King", began the development of the hotel and boarding house area until his financial empire crashed. The area on the far side of the pier, at the foot of Khyber Pass, was the Coastguard station with the Battery Parade in a semi-circle which sixty years earlier had had a battery of twelve pounder guns ready to repel Napoleon's men o' war.

Opposite
The lower harbour around 1900; the paddle steamer "Empress of India" was used to bring in becalmed sailing vessels. Beyond her is a string of rowing boats which were hired to visitors, and beyond them the cobles drawn up on a sandy stretch which is now covered by the fish quay. The first building on the left of the picture was the Scarborough and Whitby Brewery. (Photo: Thomas Watson).

this beck is now culverted under Bagdale but was open as late as the 1900s. The stream originates in the fields beyond Aislaby but nowadays is almost invisible and can never have been – by its banks – more than a stream, yet the engineers who built the piers devised a series of wood dams and brought down the blocks of stone, stage by stage to the harbour, presumably on a raft – with wood barrels for

flotation? Their ingenuity knew no bounds. I do not dispute that there was a greater flow of water than now because, like many other streams, much more of the flow is abstracted for reservoirs than in those days.

So the harbour was available again to the fishing community; their activities went on in the lower harbour whilst in the upper harbour the shipbuilding yards spread along both

The saga of Whitby's piers is unending, from the days when the stone sections were extended only to find that the extra length caused more sand to be brought in, to 1908 when the wood and concrete extensions were begun. The equipment was known as "The Walking Man" and the work took five years to complete; over recent years attempts have been made to resurface the concrete with one contractor giving the North Sea best after three years . . . (Photo: Thomas Watson).

banks. This was the time, from 1750 onwards, when Whitby's importance rapidly grew; the reason dated back to the previous century when, in three short successful wars against the Dutch we captured their merchant fleet, and the ships were sold at cut prices to Englishmen – so taking over the important Dutch trade. When these ships needed replacing the existing shipyards, which were then around the Thames and the south coast, were not interested in changing from their usual designs and the outcome was the establishment of new yards from Hull up to Newcastle devoted to building to the successful Dutch pattern.

These were generally known as "Cats" – for no traceable reason. The name of "Cat" lives on in only one unexpected context, that of pantomime; Dick Whittington, thrice Lord Mayor of London, was a Hull man who went to London with his cat – surely more likely to have been his mode of transport than a four legged beastie?

Whitby's population rose, between 1750 and 1790, from 5,000 to 14,000 according to a report produced for the Lord Lieutenant in 1796 when the country was threatened by the French. The shipbuilding industry paid steady wages. and not only were the farmers denuded of their young workers but lads who would have joined the fishing community saw a brighter future either in building or in going to sea on ships whose main job was steady work carrying coals from Newcastle to London. Among those who came to be apprenticed was James Cook, a farm labourer from Great Ayton who had taken a job as an assistant in a general store at the fishing village of Staithes and then gravitated to be an apprentice to John Walker, a Whitby shipowner, before becoming an international explorer.

Up to October 1831 the harbour light used at the end of the West Pier was a large copper lantern; a lighthouse was obviously needed to guide the increasing number of ships using the port and in just eleven weeks, starting on the 27th April, a "very handsome fluted Doric column, 75 feet high, including a rusticated base below and an octagonal light-room above, which terminated in a dome, and surrounded by a gallery, was erected. It was first lighted on the night of the 5th October, the lights being shown at high water, and for two hours before and after and visible at sea for a distance of fifteen nautical miles." The East Pier lighthouse was built in 1854 – soon after a

A storm in 1959 damaged the piers; the sea broke into the east pier and forced its way up through the surface, shifting tons of stonework. On the West Pier even larger blocks were shifted thirty and forty yards.

further lengthening of the pier had been completed. The present 500 feet long wood and concrete extensions were erected between 1908 and the outbreak of the War in 1914.

In 1817 there was a large fishing fleet registered at Whitby, with a contract to supply fish to a merchant operating in the Strand, London; he had agents who purchased on the quayside at Whitby and the fish were transported by sea or by panniers on horses. The large boats were decked-in yawls each carrying two cobles and their season started in March, going out to the Dogger Bank on a Monday and returning on Friday night. Fish is a perishable commodity and much of it was salted before it left; one of Whitby's first roads was the Salt – or Fish – Road, from Saltwick Bay to Saltersgate some ten miles over the moors. Salt was brought in by large droves of ponies, donkeys or horses each carrying two deep pannier-baskets slung across the back from mines in Cheshire; the salting of fish was officially done on the quayside but Customs men were there to levy a tax on salt and the inn at Saltersgate became – for a time – the best place to do the job and there were large cellars where the salt fish were laid out before being packed in panniers for the horses to carry. The Salt Road still exists, but diverted a little around the boundary of that more modern invention, the Fylingdales Early Warning Radar Station. There was other traffic in fish, particularly from the village of Staithes, ten miles north of Whitby, and these "pannierman's tracks" joined up across the moors; Staithes was used by Aberdeen fishermen in the 1850s who brought in their early season catches which were transported to York and the West Riding of Yorkshire. In 1860 a carrier Thomas Wake was able to deliver fish to York in one day by horse and carriage, changing horses at Malo Cross which stands on the moor behind Fylingdales Early Warning Station to this day. With the arrival of George Stephenson and his railways the traffic began to decline from 1836 onwards but many of the paths remain, marked by a row of stone paving – on which the pannierman walked. The horse-trod alongside has been mostly grown over. Who laid out the stones? Surely not the carriers? One 18th century writer suggests they may date from Lady Hilda's time, to guide pilgrims across the moors to the abbey.

The model bears a plaque reading:

A MODEL OF
H.M.S. RESOLUTION.
IN WHICH
CAPTAIN JAMES COOK. R.N. F.R.S.
MADE HIS SECOND AND THIRD VOYAGES
TO THE
SOUTH SEAS. 1772 1775. 1776 1780.
BUILT AT WHITBY BY Mr. THOS FISHBURN 1770

DIMENSIONS
GUN DECK 110ft 8in.	BEAM 30ft 5½in.
KEEL 93ft 6in.	DEPTH 13ft 1½in.
TONNAGE 462.	MEN 112.
THE CASE WAS PRESENTED BY R. LIONEL FOSTER ESQ.

Above
"HMS Resolution", the second Whitby-built ship bought by the Admiralty for Captain James Cook's voyages; like the others she had been built as a cargo boat to carry coal from Newcastle to London and converted to carry additional crew and guns at a Thames Royal shipyard. The basic round-bottomed snub shape remained ideal for beaching on Pacific Islands or scraping over coral reefs, but surely a certain recipe for seasickness. This model is in Whitby Museum.

Opposite, top
Imagination and artist's licence come together in an old painting reputed to be of Cook's ship "Endeavour", then the "Earl of Pembroke", being built at Fishburn's yard in the upper harbour. The large building could be Fishburn's house – now long demolished – but the ship was built to carry coal from Newcastle to London and was never painted up as the picture suggests. Nor did she return to Whitby to be re-fitted when the Admiralty bought her so the stern cabin is suspect.

Opposite, bottom
Titled "A Coaster unloading at Whitby", this picture gives some idea of the rig of a "Whitby Cat" engaged in trading along the coast, and in which James Cook learned his seamanship. About 100 feet long with 29ft beam and 13ft draught, they carried a crew of 17, but Cook set out from Plymouth with 94 officers, scientists and crew, plus two greyhounds and a goat!

In 1957, Matthew and Martha Winspear at home in a typical east side cottage. Bed rooms there were, but many of the homes on the harbourside had bed-places – almost a cupboard in the wall. The plank bases were frequently loose so that smuggled goods could be hidden underneath – and how many Customs officers would rouse a sleeping child during their searches?

Boulby Bank, Whitby, around 1930; the three-storey tenements housed about twenty families with one outside cold tap and two outside toilets. The tall buildings at the lower side of Church Street were mostly warehouses and were demolished to give an open harbour vista. Boulby Bank was demolished in the 1950s to make way for modern housing. It was in tenements such as these that the doubling of the population in the period from 1750 onwards was accommodated, for there is no record of additional housing being built for the influx of shipyard workers. (Photo: Hugh Lambert Smith).

2. Whitby and the Whaling Industry

British fishermen in general and Whitby's men in particular seem not to have been enthusiastic about going after whales in the Arctic circle until almost 150 years after hunting first started. The English have been credited with founding the industry around 1600 through their trading with Archangel, and the hunting area was around Spitzbergen, but in 1613 a whaling war broke out when other maritime nations moved in – Dutch, Spaniards, Danes French and "Hamburghers" – and in 1618 international allocations were agreed to sort things out, at which point the English withdrew, it would seem because the foreigners had more experience and their governments were offering bigger inducements than ours. By the beginning of the 18th century they killed most of the whales around Spitzbergen and new grounds had to be found further west, off Greenland and the Davis Straits.

The English Parliament, early in the 1700's, woke up to the fact that we were depending on imported whale oil and that supplies were intermittent due to our perennial involvement in wars with the Dutch and French, our suppliers. Whale oil was a major lubricant and it was used for street lighting; whalebone (actually from the fins of the animals) was even more valuable for it became malleable when heated and held whatever shape it was moulded to, as it cooled. So, apart from the stays for ladies' corsets, it was used for sieves and riddles, fencing, trellising, blinds for windows, bed bottoms in place of sacking, chair and sofa backs and, of course, whalebone hair brushes. It was an all-purpose ingredient in manufacturing processes – much as are modern plastics.

But Whitby was busy with other things; there was the coastal coal trade from Newcastle to London, there was the carrying of coal to the alum workings along the coast and the transport of the alum to where it was wanted. There was the trade in transporting troops in the numerous wars and skirmishes. Parliament offered a bounty of 20 shillings per ton of the ships burthen to encourage the hunting of whales but only five boats took advantage and returned with eleven whales. In 1749 the Government upped their bounty to 40 shillings and "the great revival of British whaling may be said to have begun", said Captain William Scoresby, the most successful of Whitby's whale hunters. Whitby shipowners joined the northern fishery in 1753. The price of whale oil was increasing and had risen from £10 a ton to £29 by 1754. In 1753 two Whitby vessels took part, the *Henry and Mary* under Captain Todd which killed three whales, and the *Sea Nymph* under Captain Simpson. Three years later the *Henry and Mary* was lost at sea, and the *Sea Nymph* a year later, the first of eighteen Whitby ships to be lost in the northern whaling years.

Obviously the relatively high wages paid would attract fishermen from their local offshore work but the hazards were great – ships trapped and stoved in by the ice, the perils of chasing large animals in small boats where the flick of a tail could upset the crew into icy waters with a very short hope of survival, added to the risks of sailing relatively small boats in Arctic seas and gales. Even the joy of sighting the home port could be dashed by a reception committee of the Press Gang wanting stalwart men for His Majesty's navy, which did happen; there is a record of one seaman, being taken off a whaling ship as it

Above

The Greenland whaler "Baffin" was built at Liverpool and launched in February 1820, and began her maiden voyage a month later. "Baffin" was specially fitted for the Greenland whaling fishery. She was lost in the Davis Straits in 1830; for a time Captain William Scoresby Jnr. was in command. He and his father, also William, were Whitby's famous whaling men. William Senior lived from 1760 to 1829, and his son from 1798 to 1859.

Right

Part of a page of the whaling log book from Scoresby's ship "Resolution", giving the date and who caught the whales.

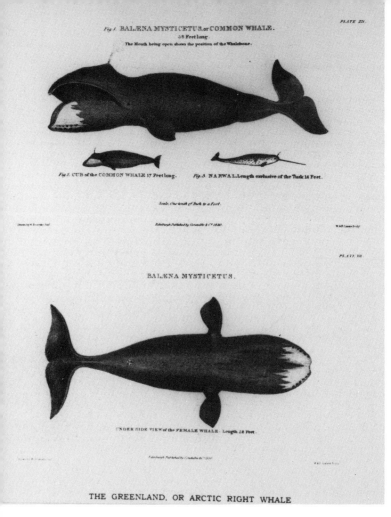

Left
Drawings by William Scoresby Junior from his "Account of the Arctic Regions" showing the Balena whale which occurred in enormous numbers in the Greenland Sea. From it was taken the whalebone used in commerce, the length of bone being usually about one fifth the length of the "fish" and found in the upper jaw. The book, like others, uses the term "fish" when it is actually a mammal.

Right
An illustration in Scoresby's book shows one of the perils of whaling; the harpooner and his crew, flicked with their boat into the air by the whale's tail, would be in immediate danger of hypothermia from the icy water.

Below
From a painting of whaling ships returning to Whitby harbour, but the artist has not shown the ships with a whale's tail in the rigging as was usual after a successful voyage. According to records, the cliffs would have been lined with wives and sweethearts watching for the return.

came into Whitby and being forced to row the naval dinghy out to the waiting man o'war, who forced his legs against the planking, stove it in and successfully swam for shore, but many other local fishermen were taken. The odd thing is that the Press Gang was illegal – there was never any authority from Parliament for the activity; what a heyday our modern exponents of the rights of the individual would have had! Probably a clout from a marlin spike and a shove into the bottom of the boat would have stopped all protesting very rapidly.

Recent researches by this author into Customs and Excise records of the time have brought out some previously unpublished papers which show that the owners of whaling ships had to prove their vessels seaworthy, their victualling sufficient, and the crew experienced to a Customs inspecting officer. It was the Customs department that dealt with the paper work for payment of bounties and laid down the procedures before a ship could go to sea. There was a bonus of £500 for the vessel arriving back with the greatest quantity

of oil, £400 for the second and so on to the fourth and fifth boats. On the tonnage of a boat depended the number of fishing lines, harpoons and small boats it must carry, and in every case six months provisions was specified, "the account to be given in writing and sworn before the Customs Collector." For the visit of this officer the master, surgeon and crew were mustered on the quarter deck; he could turn down the surgeon if he had not enough experience as well as any of the harpooners, boat steerers, line managers, and greenmen if he was not satisfied. An apprentice had to be twelve years and under twenty years of age when bound and the indenture must be for three years at least; if the officer was doubtful of his age, then the captain had to produce the parochial register. It would seem that precautions were being taken with the crew for this hazardous occupation, whilst the ship needed to be stronger than ordinarily to withstand the pack ice. The hull had to be "doubled and fortified" and there is a record of the *Resolution*,

The lower harbour, circa 1800, viewed from the area of the present Scotch Head bandstand; the puzzle is the flight of steps in the right foreground of which no trace remains.

Scoresby's ship, costing £7,791 to build plus another £471 for strengthening. The largest item in her fitting out was £1091 for wood casks.

The Whitby whaling activities stopped altogether from 1759 to 1766 following the outbreak of the seven years' war with France. The transport of troops proved profitable whilst the activities of French privateers in the North Sea made it dangerous to sail without the protection of a man o'war; there was a penalty of £1,000 for an infringement of a rule requiring ships to sail in convoy which led to problems at Whitby where laden ships could only leave harbour at spring tides "and could not therefore wait in harbour until a Vessel of War arrived" to shepherd them, so when

whaling restarted in 1767 the Customs officer Peter Maxwell asked their Lordships in London to be pleased to grant a licence for the Northern Whale Fishery to proceed on their voyage as soon as occasion offered for them quitting the harbour. The ships were listed, as well as the armament they carried which would have seemed enough to look after themselves; the *Volunteer* had eight carriage guns, six 4-pounders, two Carronades 18-pounders, four swebles with muskets, blunderbusses, lances and cutting knives.

Over the next twenty years Whitby's fleet increased to twenty ships. "The bounty was not the only incentive; the price of whalebone maintained a high level, especially as in 1771 the consumption of whalebone in the stiff stays used by ladies was very great." An idea of the financial returns gained from one voyage in the 1770s is given by "The Authentic Narration of the Voyage of the Volunteer From Whitby" written by a gentleman surgeon on the ship. Five whales were caught filling 186 butts (wood casks) with blubber which boiled down to 65 tons of oil selling at a minimum price of £20 a ton. The whalebone sold at £600 a ton. The total was £1,300 for the oil and £2,300 for the bone, £4,000 gross.

The ships arrived back at Whitby between the middle of July and the end of August. Under the government decree they had to remain within the limits of the Greenland Seas for sixteen weeks, and it took two weeks to reach the fishing grounds. "One can well imagine the growing unrest and excitement in Whitby as the time drew near for the arrival of the ships, the crowds of wives and children waiting day by day on the cliff tops to catch the first glimpse with garlands flying at the masthead and a pair of whale jaws triced up the rigging to show the ship was full." The two Whitby captains most renowned were William Scoresby Senior (1760-1829), inventor of the crow's nest, and his son also William who started as mate to his father and in later life, after all the slaughter of wildlife, became a minister of the Church of England. The senior Scoresby is credited with, in the course of thirty years, no less than 533 whales yielding 4,664 tuns of oil and 240 tons of whalebone, plus many thousands of seals, some hundreds of walruses, very many narwhals and sixty polar bears. "He even succeeded in taming a polar bear which he brought home and kept on a chain near a cask of water at the corner of Spital Bridge, in Church Street near his home. It escaped once "to the great alarm of the inhabitants but, taking with him a stout rope, he walked up to the great animal and, putting the rope over its head, led it quietly back to his ship."

The totals brought into Whitby over fifty years from 1766 to 1816 were:- whales 2,761; seals 25,000; polar bears 33; unicorns (narwhals) 43; sea horses 64.

In the upper harbour great boiler houses were built "where the gasworks now are and here the blubber was reduced down to oil and the residue converted to manure, distilling a perfume which made strong men pale and brave men weep". It should be added that at the same time the alum trade was busy and the solvent used in extracting from the rock was stale urine, which was collected in barrels placed around the streets of the town. There must have been no escape from vile odours.

The decline in the whale fishery was caused by overfishing and extensive slaughtering of whales in the Greenland Seas – a lesson not learned in the 20th century when the herring was virtually fished out. The trade finished completely in Whitby in 1837 after a succession of ships returned "clean" – with nothing caught. At the same time a Southern Whale Fishery had started around the Falkland Islands and South Georgia where the sperm whale was abundant. Processing factories were set up in the islands and it is interesting to note, in these days of problems with the Argentine and the desire of the Falkland population to stay British, that in the 1800s out of a population of 1,337 at least 1,000 were natives of Norway and Sweden. In 1832 there were 800 ships employing 10,000 seamen which produced a gross of 4 million dollars, whilst the Northern Fishery had 81 ships, 4,000 seamen and grossed £125,000.

Uses for whale products were becoming less. The advent of gas from coal was replacing whale oil in street lighting, and "the use in the manufacture of ladies stays had declined by 1818, some ladies having superseeded its use by supporting themselves with plates of steel". It came to the point where whale oil was worth very little and only the price of whalebone made it worthwhile and the industry faded away. The writer E. Keble Chatterton summed it up, "If some of the astute old whaling skippers and hardened harpooners could come back today (1930) and learn that a fleet of 55 Steam Catchers had killed in one Antarctic season 9,915 whales and made £3,056,860 for their owners, we should find some interesting comments." What they would have thought of the 1980s when conservation is the name of the

Selling fish and crabs was another job for the ladies of the fishing families. (Photo: F. M. Sutcliffe).

game, we can only conjecture.

According to ancient rights, whales, dolphins, porpoises and, of course, sturgeon, if captured in territorial water or stranded or washed ashore, dead or alive, belonged to the Crown. Whales were valued for their flesh and oil. The flesh when salted was considered, in the Middle Ages, so costly a delicacy that it was reserved for the tables of royalty and those of highest rank. It was regarded as a reward to the king for his protection of peaceful merchants and other seafarers by his navy from attacks by pirates and sea robbers – as far back as the Dukes of Normandy and the ancient kings of Denmark before that.

In the time of Henry II "any Royal fish caught in the Thames was taken to the Tower and there cut up by the Constable acting for the King". Barrels of salted whale were taken by the king when going to Palestine in 1392. There is an old legend that the head and body of the whale were sent to the king, and the tail to the Queen for her stays – which must be wrong because whalebone comes from the mouth, not the tail of the animal. The Right to Fishes Royal was given up by the Queen in 1971, and any sturgeon caught should now be sent to the mayor of the local council! Presumably when the right was established it was not known that the whale is a mammal and not a fish.

Conversation piece around 1890 pictured by F. M. Sutcliffe.

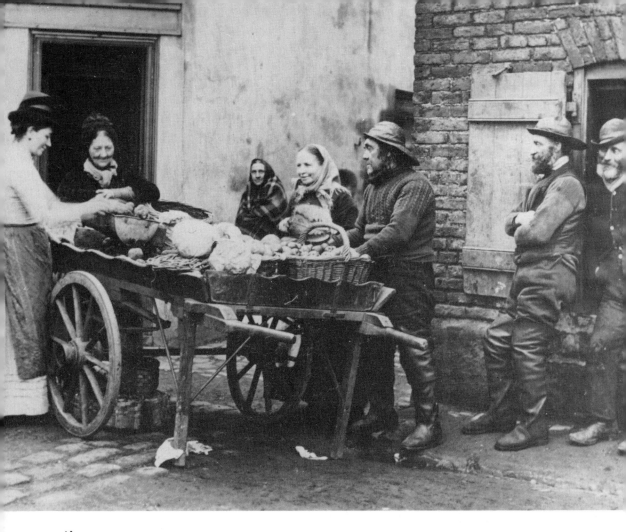

Above
Buying vegetables in Grape Lane, Whitby, which presumably came on the barrow from a local market garden – possibly where the Pannett Park now is. Had it been farmer's produce it would have been on a horse-drawn cart. (Photo: F. M. Sutcliffe).

Opposite
The modern photographer would have a job to find characters like these on the harbourside but if the weather was the topic the conversation would be much the same. (Photo: F. M. Sutcliffe).

Above
Sails and nets up to dry; a photograph by F. M. Sutcliffe early in the century, presumably taken at a weekend because the records state that the fleet stayed off the pier ends during the week.

Opposite, top
Around the turn of the century boats from Penzance in the upper harbour. (Photo: F.M. Sutcliffe).

Opposite, bottom
Salmon cobles in the foreground, rowing boats for pleasure against the quay, and local and Penzance boats setting off for the herring grounds, circa 1900. (Photo: F. M. Sutcliffe).

Above

Dock End in 1880 with the "Alert" on the right. Lying at the left are the "Sara" and "Hopewell". (Photo: F. M. Sutcliffe).

Opposite

Two centuries after Whitby's great shipbuilding days when photography was yet to be invented, this modern picture of sailing ships in harbour gives an impression of what must have been commonplace. But the clean smart ships now used for sail training and TV programmes can bear little resemblance to the coal-carrying or whaling ships of the 1700s.

3. But the local fishing had gone on . . .

Twenty or more Whitby ships to be crewed for the whaling extravaganza plus the demand for the shipbuilding industry must have denuded the number of men available for inshore fishing until the 1840s, the end of the Georgian period when Whitby's prosperity declined considerably. The alum trade had gone – poor prices caused by overproduction meant the exit of the entrepreneurs, the whaling fleet had gone, the shipbuilding rapidly declined and whilst there was a minor surge with iron and steel ships the boom days were over. This would mean a severe drop in local revenues which may have been the reason for slowness in replacing the bridge across the harbour which had become too narrow to allow the passage of the larger ships the market was requiring.

For these several reasons Whitby became a quieter place – even the worst of the smuggling era seems to have been over, and the harbourside had little but its local fishing activities. The herring shoals still came and in 1833 herring processing houses were built on Tate Hill; then the railway came and gave an impetus to that activity which was short lived, for the railway also went to Scarborough and Hartlepool and these towns boomed. Between the two, Whitby was neglected and her townspeople feverishly tried to turn her into a fashionable watering place – but that's another story.

The pattern for the fishermen would not alter; the yearly cycle of lobsters and crabs in the spring and summer, the salmon and trout catching, and fishing with mussel-baited lines in autumn and winter, the hardships of the men matched by the labours of their womenfolk who, apart from raising the children and keeping some home comforts, had the unending job of cleaning lines and baiting hundreds of hooks whilst their men were at sea. All this with the recurring poverty when bad weather kept the boats in port and there was no social security to tide them over.

That this desperation went on for many years is illustrated by a conversation a few years ago with an eighty-year old fisherman recalling a Christmas when his children were small; there had been three weeks of bad weather and there was neither money nor food in his cottage nor in his nearby parents' home. He confessed that he "went thieving". He knew from summer days spent brambling that a certain farmer kept hams in a barn near Robin Hood's Bay and it was there that he went one night, a few days before Christmas; along the beach from Whitby at low tide, up the cliffs at Saltwick Bay, and across the fields to the farm. There were no lights in the house, the farm

Opposite, top
From a painting reputedly showing the "Earl of Pembroke", later renamed "Endeavour" for James Cook's voyages, leaving Whitby harbour, circa 1767. In the left background is the solid cliff before Khyber Pass was cut. There is a simple mast on the end of the West Pier, before the lighthouse was built.

Opposite, bottom
Mussels to buy, to skein, to soak and then to fix on hundreds of hooks before the menfolk can go fishing – a process repeated almost every day for centuries.

The Dock End in the upper harbour in the 1950s with the church of St. Michael visible in the background – it is now demolished and the site is a car park.

dogs must have been asleep as he forced the barn door, unhooked a ham and was off as fast as his legs could carry him. He arrived home at three in the morning, famished, cut into the ham and put on the frying pan. "The smell must have wafted upstairs because it wasn't long before first the children and then my wife came down and we had a feast. By seven o'clock I had been round to father's and they didn't ask any questions – it was desperation days." Fish prices were low and it was usual for

the fishing families to augment their income by working at potato picking, gathering turnips, picking brambles and selling to shops in the town, anything to try and build up a small fund against even harder days.

Through all those years until the advent of motor power they were dependent on the wind and weather. No forecasts, no warnings except experience of working in a cruel North Sea. No wind at all could cause problems – the same fisherman told of four days becalmed

The oldest inhabitants flocked on to the town chimneys during the last war; locals blamed it on the coastal guns whilst ornithologists said it was an influx of other species which drove them from the cliffs. Culling has thinned them down to a level where the summer visitors' sleep is not disturbed in the early morning.

and drifting from off Whitby nearly to Hull "with a dead whale for company. As fast as we pushed it off it drifted back alongside and the smell was terrible."

The womens' work was never done. One fisherman summed it up that they did more work than the men who went to sea and certainly marriage was a working partnership. In the days before weather forecasts the man was up early – two o'clock in the morning it could be, depending on tides – to walk down the pier and look at the sea, rouse the family to make a pot of tea and see him off and then it was on with the mussels if they hand any, frequently a frozen mass which played havoc with fingers sore from the days before. Mussels were the best bait but they were costly, and had to be imported to the town; "imported" because one of the main suppliers in the early days of the 20th century was a Mrs Castleton in Ireland, whilst others came from Boston and Morecambe. Mrs Annie Leadley, a daughter of the Cole family who for at least four generations were fishing in cobles from Staithes and larger boats all named *Venus* from Whitby, recalls that they cost two shillings and ninepence (about 13p) a bag, which would bait two lines. They came by rail. The mussels had to be opened with a knife, skeined from the shells and then soaked in a large tin bath to make them bigger. "Flithers" (limpets) were the second best and could be gathered off the Scaur – the rocky foreshore stretching from the foot of the cliffs down to and below the low water mark on the south side of the East Pier at Whitby, and it was there that the wives, sisters, daughters and the older retired fishermen went, stumbling over the slippery seaweed covered rocks in the half light to scrape up the flithers from the rocks with a blunt knife.

How many baits did they need? There were 13½ score (270) hooks on a line and three or four lines at a minimum each day. Some lines were always left ashore for the women to start on, cleaning and baiting until the boat came back from sea. Chauvinism undoubtedly existed as evinced by a remark made in one family when father had got back early and gone straight to the pub – "He's not going to sit there while we sit skeining, and putting a fur coat on the landlady's back." The lines, coiled up on a board with the baited hooks laid skilfully around so that they would run out without tangling, had to be got down to the coble; "I've carried many a one on my head when I was a girl," said Annie Leadley, "but when I got married my husband made me a barrow."

You might think that baiting lines, housework, and coping with frequent pregnancies was enough for a woman's day, but not so: at Whitby some women had stalls on the quayside where they sold fish and their children gave a delivery service to the big houses around the town. Others walked for miles to outlying farms and villages carrying baskets of fish on their head – delighting the eye of early photographers who designated it as a quaint activity worth recording when in fact it was a necessary part of the family's exchequer. What else did the women do? Well, there was always a woollen jersey or long seaboot stockings to knit – and if you had a spare bedroom by doubling or trebling up in summer, you might take in visitors. "You'd do owt for an extra bob or two."

A graphic picture of life is given by the story recounted of the family of John William (Woodpeg) Storry born in 1893 in a cottage at the top of Tate Hill Pier, Whitby. His mother died giving birth to his sister when he was eighteen months old. His father was at sea at all hours and with no hope of looking after two small children so they were taken in by their grandparents, Joseph Leng and his wife, who had a bakery at the foot of the 199 Church Stairs; not only did they bake bread but they also cooked food brought in by their customers. "There was a regular trade with folks bringing in a dripping pot with a few cuttings of meat and a few slices of tatey for Grandad to put in the oven." There were also the Christmas cakes brought in for baking – and what a marvellous excuse for a housewife for if it was a success she took the credit, but a failure could be blamed on Mr Leng! The cooking of meals for twopence or threepence was often done on the "pay you next week" basis, or, as "Woodpeg" Storry put it, "on the chucky" and next week never came. There was a dilemma for the baker – or the grocer – supplying these poor fishing families for if they said enough was enough, pay up or no more, there were other establishments the customer could go to and the amount outstanding was lost for ever. So the inevitable day came when the Leng's bakery went broke, and the six years old lad with a healthy appetite went back to live with his father – where there was no woman in the house. "Father was off fishing all day and half the night and I had to look after myself and do my own mending. I used to have my stocking hanging out of my shoe toe. I used to hold my clothes together with safety pins, and sometimes there were more pins than clothes. The other lads used to laugh at me but I had no-one to help. There was no money for new things and you had to make

Above
No longer needed – the dipping of nets
made from natural fibres was a
necessity, but not with modern man-
made fibres. This tank or barking
copper, was at the Whitehall Shipyard
in the 1950s, but in earlier days there
were extensive facilities two hundred
yards further up river beyond the site of
the present high level bridge.

Right
Jim Cole in his eighties was still
occupied in the family business; the
family came from Staithes to Whitby in
the early years of the century and had a
succession of keelboats all named
"Venus".

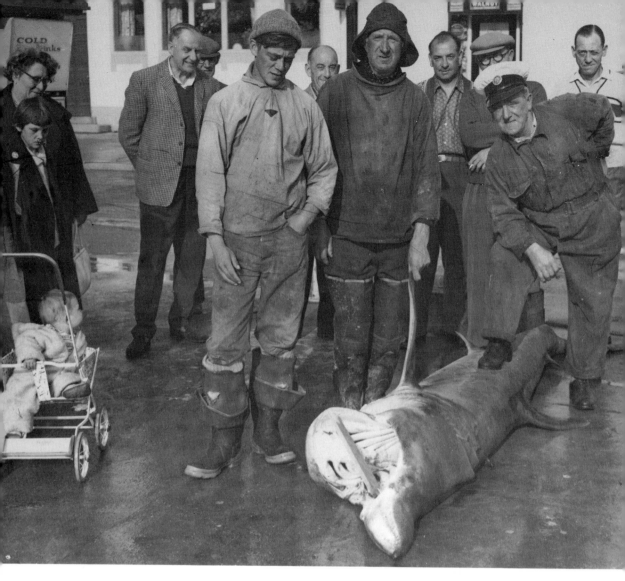

Entangled with a net, this Basking Shark caused a great deal of damage in July 1962 when Woodpeg Storrey and Matt Hutchinson (left of picture) were out salmoning. The victorious foot belonged to Tom Hutchinson, one of the harbour staff.

do. He mebbe brought home ten bob or a pound and then perhaps nothing for a fortnight. A new pair of shoes at four and elevenpence ha'penny (25p) was more than we could find."

"The youths of today don't know how lucky they are," said Woodpeg. "Many a time I had to go to school with a piece of dry bread in me pocket, no butter, not even a cup of tea. Dickie Hodgson used to have a fruit stall near the Market Hall and many a time I

pinched an apple as I ran past on the way to school."

It was starvation level. He went on to describe how he and Jim Murfield used to creep round the back of the Royal Hotel on the West Cliff and scrounge food from the kitchens. "We used to get cold pudding, or salmon or any other bits that were left over and we survived on that." Days started early for his first job was to go out on the Scaur collecting bait for his father and then getting

Taken by the author in 1972 – and not posed for the camera – this group of Staithes ladies with their traditional bonnets, busy boiling crabs, could have been taken at any time since photography was invented, apart from a give-away zip fastener on a boot! On the right of the picture is Dinah Theaker who banged the big drum in the annual Nightie Parade through the village.

back in time for school – and a late arrival meant the cane. His pocket money when he grew up a little was earned by winkle picking at Hawsker Bottoms near the High Light lighthouse. "Mary Ann 'Acky' Atkinson used to buy them off us and send them to Billingsgate by train. She gave us half a crown (12½p) for six stone." And then there was potato picking; the prospects depended on the farmer but two shillings was "about right". Woodpeg smacked his lips as he recalled working for Richardsons' at Cross Butts Farm where, whilst they only paid one and sixpence (7½p) a day, there was a good rabbit pie dinner.

"There would be about nine of us round the table, starving and she opened the door and in came the Pie. We all sat there with mouths drooling and rubbing our hands." The moment when the pie was cut and the plates filled was a vision that was still in Woodpeg's memory seventy years later.

Above
The coble fisherman's methods haven't changed, apart from some using a pot hauler; this photograph of the Whitby coble "Floral Queen" in the 1960's could just as easily have been thirty years before or after.

Left
"Floral Queen" leaving Whitby harbour needs a man standing to see over the pile of pots.

The year 1919 when Woodpeg returned from war service at sea coincided with a boom in fish prices. He went fishing in a sailing mule aptly named *Welcome Home* which, as well as a jib sail, had a small petrol engine. The fish prices were good probably as a result of shortages of imported meat and other foods due to the loss of shipping. Price comparisons can only sound ridiculous today – although no doubt the 1980s' fishermen will aver that they haven't kept up with the increased cost of everything else – but around 1920 a stone of cod fetched between five shillings and seven and sixpence (25p - 37½p); lobsters were from three halfpence to tenpence each and London buyers would pay £3 for twenty "and that was an awful lot of money to us." They might even get up to 1s 6d apiece (7½p) in Derby Week.

Another fisherman, Matt Verrill of Staithes, recalled that in 1930 "we had no pot haulers, we had everything to haul by hand and sometimes it was seventeen fathoms. Of course, there were maybe more fish in those days. We were catching bigger and better fish in the 1930s than the cobles do now. You never see a good cod landed now. Why, if we had eight of them weighing ten or twelve pounds, and they fetched twenty-five shillings you were laughing. It was a good price."

Forty-seven years later, and some things have changed. Robert Peart, a Whitby cobleman, agrees that cod are not as large as they used to be and blames it mostly on overfishing. He says that line fishing for cod is the most profitable "but there's no point in going when there's plenty of live food about – sand eels, small herrings, sprats and so on – because cod will go for live bait before they'll go for mussels on the lines."

So before March and after August – the salmon and trout season – they go potting for lobster and crabs, "the worst paid job nowadays with lobster only fetching £2.40 to £2.60 a pound, although if they're scarce they can get up to £5 a pound". They work an area from Skinningrove in the north to Ravenscar in the south and in 1986 there were more to the east of Whitby. "I think its been so overfished

on the north side, it's been hammered so there's bound to be less. The ground you're working on also governs the catch, a hard ground can mean less crabs and more lobsters, a miry ground can mean up to fifteen crabs in one pot, weighing a stone and a half. But the bait must be fresh, we have used bait a week old and they've taken it but not as many. They're scavengers, they'll eat anything, their usual food must come from the small fish that are killed by heavy weather – they get smashed to pieces. Lobsters are not as fussy, they'll eat anything. We use any small fish for bait, gurnets and whiting and the like. The pots take about 3½ hours apiece to make, there's no difference between those for crabs and lobsters. We may get a mixed catch, we may get half a dozen crabs in one pot and a lobster will follow them in, but if a lobster gets in first a crab will not go near.

"There are a couple of larger Whitby boats going with pots, they can work 900 – 1,000 pots, whereas the cobles work with 240, four strings of sixty with a marker at each end and we leave them overnight." Matt Verrill said that in 1930 they had no pot hauler and worked as deep as seventeen fathoms, but nowadays the pots are down thirty fathoms, five miles out, and couldn't be brought up without a pot hauler plus the weight of the thirty stones a day of crabs averaged in 1986. Whitby used to have a poor reputation for its crabs, mostly due to some fisherman bringing in loads of watery crabs. "It's easy to pick them out as they come up in the pots, they're soft because they've been casting their shells and are just hardening up, and the water is running out of them. The claws are purple coloured instead of black. Nowadays the watery ones aren't brought ashore."

The crab season can go on till Christmas but as soon as there is any snow water coming down, they are gone, burying themselves in the sand until it warms up the following year. In spring the men working with gill nets, which are laid on the bottom, can bring them up, especially after a heavy sea. "There's everybody but the Archbishop of Canterbury

been using gill nets off Whitby since about 1976. The fish swim into them and get entangled. They put them down on hard ground in the herring season and catch a fair amount of fish – not high class but full of feed and oil. It sells but it doesn't fetch the price of winter line-caught fish."

For the future? "The shellfish industry has declined since inshore trawling started, and with the quotas on white fish now coming in, it would seem that more boats are liable to turn to potting to make a living."

I suppose that if bread is man's staple diet from the land, then cod is the staple diet from the northern seas; gadus morrhua it was named by the erudite but more recognisable

to modern generations as the source of the fish finger. To the medical world its liver is the source of that valuable commodity cod liver oil, full of vitamins, abhorred by previous generations but nowadays delivered in capsules or even mint-flavoured to disguise its taste. Caught in millions off Iceland's coast – where the big ones are – from ships incorporating their own processing factory, from trawlers and in nets right down the North Sea, on lines cast over from cobles and even smaller boats in the coastal waters, by patient muffled-up men (and some women) with expensive rods leaning on the pier railings or on the beach, and by optimistic small boys with fishing

Left
The fish quay in 1937 before the enclosed selling area and the storage pens for equipment were erected. (Photo: H. Lambert-Smith).

Right
A short-lived business was the export of lobsters to France by Havelock Turner, seen here with Mike Kilpatrick in the 1960s.

lines; there are natural predators who take a few as, presumably, nature intended but the situation has arisen in 1987 when quotas have had to be imposed on catching cod around our coasts to allow stocks to build up again. The economics of the fishing industry will be upset, prices will rise, fish and chips become a luxury, boats will have to remain tied up in port, shipbuilders will suffer, and the blame must lie with our modern inventiveness in finding ways of catching more fish with no thought for the future; the cod on quota, the catching of salmon and trout in the tidal water of the river Esk banned for at least ten years, the ban on herring fishing just lifted, the trawling almost under the cliffs that

disturbs the breeding grounds for lobsters and crabs – and above ground the forests affected by acid rain from our power stations and even the space above the atmosphere cluttered with the bits and pieces of rocket debris, it must be nearing the time when a quota is placed on man and his activities or maybe the banning of inventions and methods which have not been approved by an environmental panel. Maybe we should ask the codfish for his opinion.

Probably the working of lines from a coble has changed least of all. Three men in a boat and the only difference between now and fifty years ago is the addition of a motor; the lines with their hooks every ten feet militate against mechanical hauling, and echo sounders and the like are seldom used unless its foggy weather and they can't see their landmarks – the motor gives them the advantage that they can get home when the wind and tide are against them, not as in the days of sailing cobles where they might have to stay and ride it out for twenty-four hours. Laurence Murfield told Skipper Dora Walker "it was surprising what some of those small cobles would live through. One day in winter three men were forced to stay out for twenty four hours. When the coble came back there were two dead men in her. The fellow who brought her in was the only one who had a meal before he set off the day before; the other two had meant to come back for one and had never had the chance. Even in a motor coble it's safest not to go to sea on an empty stomach in winter. Engines can fail!"

He went on to say that hauling lines was always done under oars, pulling up to the lines if there was any wind, and backing the oars and hauling stern first when there was none. Laurence Murfield had started fishing as a young lad and eventually crewed for Miss Dora Walker who was the only lady skipper of a coble on the coast. Miss Walker wrote several books on her experiences and on her conversations with local men as well as being a mine of information on ships and their history.

Murfield would be a lad in the 1920s and his description of the Fish Market corroborates information from similar sources; "the Fish Market," he said, "at that time was at the Coffee House End and we had to take the fish up there in baskets for the auction. Afterwards we took the boats over and moored them as near home as possible to facilitate putting the lines ashore for the family to get started with the baiting. The boys usually raced off to the railway station to see if the bags of mussels had come, or, if it was low water, dug for worms or went on the shore to look for flithers.

Line fishing starts in October and November; the most complex type of fishing that can only be learned by serving a four of five years' apprenticeship as a "dogsbody" to experienced men. Robert Peart learned that way with his father and uncle, and says that nowadays they bait their own lines when they come in, although some of the larger boats do have retired fishermen or their families baiting for them. "We do get some help in skeining the mussels." They come in six-stone sacks from Boston at (1987) £8.50 a bag. This compares with fifty years ago when they were two shillings and ninepence an eight stone bag "and those were clean – we get a lot of waste."

"We get three lines to a bag, and we use two bags a day for the six lines we use. Each line is made up of six pieces of string 60 fathoms long, and there's a hook every ten feet along. Making up a line, you use two nails 3 feet 4 inches apart, and every third turn you put a hook on, so you have about 200 hooks on a line. We don't use flithers (limpets) off the Scaur, they go off too quickly. We soak the mussels for a couple of hours, any longer and they go hard. It takes an hour and a quarter to bait a line."

"You can only go line fishing nowadays in daylight – there's so many nets and markers around – and that takes about six hours a day, another three hours baiting, then there's time on the Market and you can soon get up to twelve or thirteen hours a day; if you're working further out to sea it can well be a fourteen hour day. We can lose a lot of days with bad weather; for the last two years the wind was mostly from the east and we couldn't work but this present winter its been mostly from the south-west, off the land, and we could. You can sign on the Labour exchange and its worth about a fiver a day but at that price you'd far rather be at sea – despite the fact that we've been out days this winter when the water's been washing through you, fish boxes frozen to the deck and ice forming on the boat. It would frighten anyone who wasn't used to it. You've got to have a good crew, know where to fish, know what the tide's doing and when to shoot or you'll catch nothing."

Above
Auctioning the catch in the 1960s but little different to many years before and since.

Right
Fishing is a cold enough job without having to break the ice before you can leave the dock end in the upper harbour. Even the main stream of the river has been known to freeze.

Above
George Colley (Sack) Walker couldn't quite think of what he was going to say.

Right
John Hill occupied his retirement in a traditional way.

Above
The White Horse and Griffin Hotel in Church Street was a stage coach departure point and both Charles Dickens and Captain James Cook stayed there. It became virtually derelict for fifty years, then a net making and repairing business was set up in the main room for a few years and now is being refurbished to display waxworks. An application for a return to its old days as licensed premises was turned down by the magistrates.

Left
Tal Bennison (right) and the late Jake Cole discussing fishing as it used to be?

4. Lifeboats

Bad weather could mean a few extra shillings from lifeboat service; for many years until the advent of motor lifeboats the heavy rowing lifeboats were kept in a shed at the foot of Khyber Pass which is now in use as a Lifeboat Museum, and with the last rowing boat preserved there on its massive caterpillar wheels.

The launch was down the nearby slipway beside the West Pier and there was not only need for a crew but also for a team of launchers. Imagine the storm, the sailing ship – and sometimes more than one – battered onto the beach to the north of the pier or, worse, on to the rocky Scaur south of the harbour mouth and the only hope for the men on board was a rowing lifeboat a quarter the size of the ship in distress. The white-crested waves breaking on the beach and the launching crew manhandling the boat on its carriage into deep enough water to float it off – it was no sinecure of a job. The launchers could be up to their neck in the icy breakers not only for the launch but again, hours later, to pull it ashore again.

There were always plenty of volunteers – "it was natural to want to help", said Woodpeg Storrey, "but there was the money to think of as well." The would-be launchers gathered at the foot of the Cragg steps (between the present amusement arcades) waiting for Mr Langlands, the coxswain of the No. 1 boat. He stood half a dozen steps up and threw a handful of brass tokens in the air. "Then", said Woodpeg, "the fight commenced. You were down on the ground scrabbling for them. You got one and someone put their boot on your hand and took the skin off, anything to make you let go, but it was worth it for the three shillings and sixpence (17½p) you got."

Three shillings and sixpence for the privilege of standing neck deep in icy water to launch and again when the weary crew brought the boat back – and perhaps went straight out again after landing survivors or to replace broken oars. What happened if the storm blew up whilst the local boats were at sea? It was the women who hauled the heavy caterpillar tractor out of the shed, down the slipway across the soft sand and into the breakers.

For the volunteer crew the task ahead was indeed daunting and perilous; somewhere out there, invisible in the heavy seas, was a sailing ship in trouble and a crew to be saved. Nothing but eight fishermen at heavy oars to get to them, and the sort of waves when oars could break and the crew finish up in a blaspheming heap in the bottom of the lifeboat. Anyone could volunteer to go; lifebelts were hung on racks and the first men there got them. "You couldn't touch the belts belonging to the cox, second cox or bowman," said Woodpeg, "but there was plenty of barging around to get the others."

Whitby's lifeboat history dates back long before the days of the Royal National Lifeboat Institution to the year 1802, just four years after the first ever was built by Henry Greathead for South Shields; Lloyds of London had offered a subscription of £50 to any port purchasing a lifeboat – presumably as much to protect their insurance business as for the saving of life? – and a Whitby committee must have subscribed the rest of the £150 plus delivery costs, charged by Mr Greathead for the boat and its carriage. She arrived in November 1802 and on December 11th, according to the *Newcastle Chronicle*,

ove
e "Robert and Ellen Robson" coming
its carriage at the foot of the slipway
n awkward procedure even in calm

ht
e West Pier slipway down which the
ing lifeboats were manhandled in
s like this. Whatever else has
nged the fury of the sea has not.

At the top of the slipway.

"About eleven o'clock in the forenoon, nearly at low water, the wind blowing strong E.N.E. and the sea very high, the sloop *Edinburgh*, Joseph Poole, Master, coal laden from Sunderland, in attempting to enter the harbour grounded (as was expected) a considerable distance from the pier head. A coble, which had with some difficulty proceeded over the harbour bar for the purpose of offering assistance, being struck by a heavy sea, was instantly overset and the people, three in number, plunged into the water. Being excellent swimmers they gained the shore . . . The lifeboat (being the first time of its being employed) was brought down and launched into the water, when a party of sailors with the greatest alacrity pushed her through the heavy surf, proceeded to the *Edinburgh*, took out the crew and brought them to shore."

Over the years various boats were bought by local subscription and many rescues were made in appalling weather conditions. The crew was frequently drawn from members of the Preventive Service, later part of the Coastguard, and the fishermen seemed to

Hauling Whitby's rowing lifeboat into the lifeboat museum when she was taken out of service.

have been unco-operative I draw the conclusion that since the Preventive men were mainly employed in prevention of smuggling and the local fishermen were sympathetic to the smugglers, this was a natural reaction; however by 1829, according to the RNLI Annual Reports, there was evidence of closer co-operation between the Coastguard and the fishermen. I would strongly recommend the book *Rowing Lifeboats of Whitby* by A. F. Humble (1974) as essential reading on this subject.

Two events in Whitby's lifeboat history

belong in this present book because of their major character and the involvement of the fishing community. February 9th, 1861 was marked by a full gale from the North East, high seas and a succession of vessels in distress. At eight o'clock in the morning some Whitby men were walking along the beach at low tide when the Sunderland brig *John and Ann* was seen aground and in distress off Sandsend; the men, six of them Whitby lifeboatmen, John Storr, John Dixon, Robert Leadley, George Martin, William Dryden and Henry Freeman, took out a Sandsend coble and saved five men

aboard the brig with great difficulty. By 10 a.m. the fishermen were back in Whitby to find that the lifeboat was being brought out to attempt the rescue of the crew of the schooner *Gamma* which was four hundred yards from the pier. The lifeboat and its carriage were hauled by a team of four horses along Pier Road, down the slipway and to the water's edge. John Storr took charge and was joined by the others from the Sandsend rescue plus John Philpot, Matthew Leadley, Christopher Collins, R. Stainthorpe, and his own brothers Thomas and William Storr, making a crew of twelve all with lifeboat experience except Henry Freeman. The crew of the *Gamma* were brought ashore, wet to the skin as were the lifeboat crew and the launchers who hauled the boat out of the surf back on to its carriage.

By 11.30 a.m. the *Clara*, a Sunderland-built barque, was aground half a mile along the beach; the rocket firing apparatus was dragged along the sands but failed to make contact as their line broke. The lifeboat was made ready – with the same crew "for there was keen competition to get into the boat. No man who failed to take his place at once subsequently regained it" – which bears out Woodpeg Storrey's recollections in his time that the money paid was of great importance. The *Clara's* crew of eleven had taken refuge in the rigging, as was usual when waves were breaking clean over a stranded vessel, except for the cook who was discovered in the bottom of the boat. All were rescued, just in time, for minutes later the ship rolled over and broke up.

At about one o'clock the brig *Utility* was driven ashore north of the Battery Parade. A few minutes later the schooner *Roe* was flung on the sand nearby. By this time Thomas Storr

had had to go and see to his coble which had broken adrift and there was competition for his place in the crew, which resulted in her going out with an extra man on board. Every man of those who had been continuously wet for hours had taken off their lifebelts and it was the possession of these which gave a place in the lifeboat. Henry Freeman had found a sample cork belt which he wore all day which fitted over the shoulders whereas the others were worn round the waist – a matter of import later. The boat was launched to the *Roe*, picked up her crew and went on the *Utility*, and returned to the beach where the tide was rising rapidly, and up the slipway. The horses were hitched on to the carriage and she was brought to the top. The seas were breaking over the pier, broken timbers swept up with it and it was deemed impossible to make any more launches until two hours after high water – which would make it around six o'clock. However at two o'clock two vessels were seen approaching the port and as their only chance of safety was to try and make it into the harbour they were signalled in. The first, the schooner *Flora*, came in safely except for some damage when she hit Tate Hill Pier. The second schooner, the *Merchant*, attempted to follow her but her sails gave way and she was carried on to the beach between the wrecks of the *Utility* and *Roe*.

The sequel was reported in the *Yorkshire Gazette*: The lifeboat was soon launched, manned with the same crew. They had some difficulty in getting to the ship as there was a very heavy sea running, and there was a schooner between the shore and the vessel they were going to. However they succeeded in getting to the vessel once but were driven back again by a

Opposite, top
For ten years from 1882 there was a lifeboat regatta in which boats from Whitby, Upgang, Robin Hood's Bay and Staithes took part.

Opposite, bottom
One of the pre-RNLI boats, locally funded, was hung from these davits on the east side and there was originally a protective shed. The davits were demolished in the 1980s by a Borough Council team.

nasty cross sea, which came round both ends of the vessel and drove them back several times. At length, two waves meeting the wave rebounding from the ship on the beach, culminated in one point and spurted up in what is called by nautical men 'the knot of a sea'. This spurting up of the waves immediately under the bottom of the lifeboat threw her completely out of the water, and a sea took her broadside on and turned her right over. The sight, the shrieks, the moans, the anxiety of mind will not readily be forgotten; to see the poor men floating about, and no assistance could be rendered them. Only one man, Henry Freeman, was saved, and this was entirely by the life-belt he had on.

The overturned boat drifted ashore; two men were under her but both were dead when brought out. The crew of the *Merchant* were saved by a line carrying a cradle and fired from a mortar by the Coastguard service.

The day's disasters were not yet over; at four o'clock the brig *Urania* went ashore near the second Nab, and the crew were eventually brought ashore after the tide had fallen. At seven o'clock the *Tribune* of Brixham came ashore. Whitby had an old lifeboat which was kept on the east side of the harbour and this was eventually brought round on the carriage and launched at around eleven o'clock with a scratch crew of master mariners, a mate, three seamen, a fisherman and two jet ornament manufacturers. They successfully rescued the crew of this eighth ship to go aground in the bay – out of a total of 210 ships lost around the coast in that one storm.

The outcome for Whitby was union of the local committee with the RNLI, who agreed to provide a new boat, an appeal for subscriptions for the families of the lost crew who had left ten widows and forty-four children (the appeal raised £5,000), and a decision to order twenty-four cork lifebelts. There was also a memorial erected in St. Mary's Parish Church, there to this day in the entrance porch; it was placed there by the rector, Rev. W. Keane who, in appealing for donations for the families, wrote a letter to the London *Times* which is inscribed verbatim on the memorial, as follows:

> We have had a fearful storm today. Half a mile of our strand is already strewn with seven wrecks; our new lifeboat, but launched a few months ago, was manned by the finest picked seamen of Whitby. Five times during the day they have braved the furious sea, and five times returned with crews from vessels in distress. A sixth ship was driven in behind the pier. The men, exhausted though they were, again pulled out but, before they had gone fifty yards, a wave capsized the boat. Then was beheld by several thousand persons, within almost a stone's throw but unable to assist, the fearful agonies of those powerful men, buffeting within the fury of the breakers till, one by one, twelve out of the thirteen sank and only one is saved. There were ten widows, forty-four fatherless children, and two dependents."

I feel that one point needs to be made; the crews of the rowing boats were pulling a heavy boat through seas rough enough to have already put larger ships in danger. The oars frequently snapped. Those same oars, by their length, would hinder going alongside another ship unless they were taken in – so losing steerage on the lifeboat. Undoubtedly the men were strong as well as courageous, borne out by an exercise in the 1980s when the existing preserved rowing lifeboat was taken out by the crew of the present motor lifeboat in a calm sea from Whitby to Robin Hood's Bay, just down

Opposite
The memorial in St. Mary's Parish Church, Whitby, to the life-boatmen lost in the 1861 disaster. The Grecian temple style is out of character with both the event and the church, but took the fancy of Rev. W. Keane, Rector of Whitby, when he saw it in London.

Reputedly a photograph of the crew which took a lifeboat by road through deep snowdrifts to Robin Hood's Bay in 1891. The coxwain, with a medal on his jumper, was Henry Freeman, sole survivor of the 1861 disaster.

the coast. The most printable comment was "Never again!"

In the years that followed Whitby had other rowing lifeboats, two stationed in Whitby and another halfway towards Sandsend at Upgang – the slipway there was washed away in the 1930s and there is now no trace of the lifeboat station, or the inn and cottages nearby.

Henry Freeman became coxswain of the Whitby No. 1 lifeboat, a post he held for 22 years until he retired in 1899. He was succeeded by Thomas Langlands who had been coxswain of the Upgang lifeboat for 25 years. He was well used to the rowing lifeboats which were all they had but by 1912 the Whitby fishing boats were being motorised and there

was hope that a motor lifeboat could be supplied, a hope that was dashed with the outbreak of war in 1914 but made inevitable in the long run by Whitby's second major incident soon after the war started and which convinced everyone that rowing boats were obsolete.

On Thursday, October 29th, 1914 the *Rohilla*, built as a cruise ship but commandeered for use as a hospital ship, left Leith Docks, Edinburgh for Dunkirk to take on wounded. She was 7,409 tons, 460 feet long and took twenty-four feet of water, She had a full crew and medical staff, 229 persons in all. She was routed fairly close inshore in a bid to avoid minefields and by 3.30 a.m. on Friday morning she was off Sandsend when, in a very rough sea and a long way off her proper course, she hit something. The captain thought it was a mine exploding and he tried to run the *Rohilla* ashore.

There were sentries stationed on both Whitby's piers and one of them, sheltering in the lee of the West Pier lighthouse, was horrified to see this large ship looming out of the darkness and, he thought, straight towards the pier. The Coastguard, at his post on the 200 feet high East Cliff, had already seen her and knew that she was on course to hit Whitby Rock, just south of the East Pier and marked by a bell and light buoy – but the bell had been silenced and the light turned out because of the war. The Coastguard sounded the foghorn and signalled with a morse lamp, to no avail. *Rohilla* struck the rocks near Saltwick Nab, about a mile south of Whitby with engines going full speed ahead. It was 4.10 a.m.

She was only 600 yards from shore but the position was inaccessible and difficult for the rescue services. *Rohilla* was already breaking up with the rough seas and the fact that a third of her length was hanging over the edge of the Scaur rock with a precipitous drop below. Whitby had two lifeboats; the *Robert and Mary Ellis* still preserved in the Whitby lifeboat museum which was then the lifeboat house, and the smaller No. 2 boat *John Fielden* which

was kept moored in the harbour. It was impossible to launch the No. 1 boat down the slipway because the rough seas would have dashed it off its carriage before there was sufficient depth to float. The No. 2 boat would not have survived in the seas. By 4.45 a.m. Thomas Langlands and his crew were ready but could do nothing but wait for daylight and the chance that the seas would abate. The Coastguard were attempting to fire rockets across the *Rohilla* but she was at the limit of their range; one that did land could not be reached by the men on board the ship. All but one of her small boats had been washed away and at daybreak this survived to reach the shore with a line from the ship to establish communication, but the line snapped before it could be used. The only hope left was the lifeboat.

Langlands had an idea; there was – and is – a gap between the East Pier and the East Cliff, partly closed by a breakwater eight feet high, which leads on to the Scaur. If a lifeboat could be carried through there, and taken on her carriage nearer to the wreck, he might be able to do something. The lifeboat and its carriage weighed over three tons but volunteers flocked down to the harbour and manhandled it over the breakwater; piles of materials had been made on the other side of the eight feet drop to break the fall but even so the *John*

ON THE COAST – THE WHITBY LIFEBOAT ON ITS WAY TO ROBIN HOOD'S BAY

In 1951 the "Palmira" sank in a great storm, north of Staithes; both the Whitby coxswain, Will Richardson, and the Runswick & Staithes cox, Tom Patton, decided independently that the storm was so great they would have put their crews at risk if they had launched. The crew of the "Palmira" were lost, and an RNLI official enquiry was held which attracted a great deal of media attention. Both coxswains were exonerated, but a few months later, on November 11th, 1951, the lifeboat station at Runswick Bay was closed. These photographs show Will Richardson and Tom Patton after the result of the enquiry was made known (left); and the lifeboat leaving Runswick for the last time (above).

Mrs Laura Parkin and Mrs Mary Wompra collecting for Staithes & Runswick Bay lifeboat.

Fielden was damaged in two places. However, she was labouriously hauled the mile to Saltwick by 145 men and women – each of whom eventually received six shillings for their work. Langlands and his crew climbed in and the *John Fielden* was alongside the *Rohilla* at 9.45 a.m., five and a half hours after she struck the rocks. Seventeen people were rescued, including five nurses – one of whom had survived the sinking of the *Titanic*. The lifeboat went out again and took off another eighteen survivors but on the way ashore the damage to her hull was made worse by hitting rocks and it

was obviously suicidal to take her out a third time.

The *Rohilla* had now broken in two; the stern section overhanging the Scaur rock had broken away and the men on it were lost. The remainder were clustered near the bridge and could be seen by the thousands of people gathered on the cliffs and shore but unable to do anything to help. It was decided to haul the Upgang lifeboat to a point on the cliff above the wreck, where it was lowered down by teams of men with heavy ropes, and this was accomplished but the sea was too rough to launch. The Teesmouth motor lifeboat set out at 5 a.m. the following morning but was disabled and had to be towed back to Middlesbrough. The Scarborough rowing lifeboat was towed by a tug to arrive off the wreck by 5 p.m. but it was too dark to attempt to go alongside. They tried again on Saturday morning but by then the Scarborough crew were cold, wet and hungry and unable to pull their boat to the *Rohilla* so were towed back to Scarborough. The *Robert and Mary Ellis*, Whitby's No. 1 boat, was towed out with Langlands and his crew on board but were unable to get near. The Upgang boat was launched from the beach but was swung round by a giant wave and thrown back to the shore.

It was decided to call out the steam-powered lifeboat from Tynemouth, and it took her eight hours to cover the forty-four miles to Whitby harbour in the storm. The *Henry Vernon* sailed out of Whitby at 6 a.m. on the Sunday morning, reached the remains of the wreck and by dint of pouring oil on the water managed to get alongside and take off the last fifty survivors. Coxswain Langlands and Second Coxswain Richard Eglon received the Gold Medal of the Lifeboat Institution, as did two of the Tynemouth crew, and also a Whitby man George Peart "who had spend many hours on the beach at Saltwick and behaved with conspicuous bravery in going into the sea and saved many of those who jumped overboard from the wreck."

Rowing lifeboats were outdated. Their crews had been heroic, but the *Rohilla* disaster could have been much less if a powered lifeboat had been available on the Friday morning. Three days later an appeal was launched for funds to buy such a boat for Whitby and the *Margaret Harker Smith* was on station at the end of May 1919, five years later, a delay partly caused by the war and considerably by the local authority who objected to the proposed site for the boathouse and, that being settled, further sought to induce the RNLI to contribute to the cost of the road to the new building! This first

motor lifeboat, which was also equipped with sails in case of engine failure, was on station at Whitby until 1938, was called out 117 times and saved 86 lives. Her successor, the *Mary Ann Hepworth*, remained until 1974, was called out 372 times and saved 201 lives. Both these lifeboats were launched from the specially built house and slipway on the east side of the harbour. In 1974 a new style boat which remained permanently afloat, *The White Rose of Yorkshire*, was donated by a Harrogate lady and is to be replaced this year. *White Rose* has been called out 262 times to date, and is a fast, powerful craft; for the crew the most noteworthy event must be that in April 1982 when she was launched in a Force 8 gale to a broken-down motor fishing vessel four miles off the coast and, after towing her for four hours, handed her over to a sister ship from the Tyne. As *White Rose* attempted to enter Whitby harbour she was hit by three large waves estimated at 25 feet high and breaking. The lifeboat corkscrewed and fell into the trough of the waves on her side; injured crew members included one with four broken ribs, one with a broken arm and one with a head injury. Unable to make it into Whitby the lifeboat headed south for Scarborough. The RNLI presented their "Thanks on Vellum" to the coxswain, Peter Thomson, for the service.

Peter Thomson was a member of the crew of the previous boat, is cox of the present boat and will take over his third boat later in the year (1987); she will be a Tyne Class boat with a top speed of 18 knots with a watertight aluminium wheelhouse which makes the boat self-righting in five seconds. She will be fitted with medium and very high frequency radios, radar, automatic direction-finding units, echo sounders, intercom system and a Decca Navigator. She will once again be slipway launched from the existing house. Whatever her name, she will be the 28th boat – apart from the inflatable inshore craft which first arrived in 1966 – to carry on a tradition of Whitby lifeboats by which, since the days when the RNLI took over from the local organisation, 1,190 lives have been saved.

Above
Robin Hood's Bay lifeboat in 1893, the "Ephraim and Hannah Fox". The extensive rocky scaur must have been a great hazard for the local fishing fleet as well as for launching the lifeboat in the rough seas when she would be needed. There is no longer a lifeboat stationed there.

Right
The "Mary Ann Hepworth", a motor lifeboat at Whitby for many years.

Above
The "Robert & Ellen Robson" was the last rowing lifeboat at Whitby, and also the last in the RNLI fleet; she is preserved in Whitby Lifeboat Museum on the West Pier.

Opposite, top
The "White Rose of Yorkshire", the present Whitby boat, was paid for by a Harrogate lady.

Opposite, bottom
A Tyne class boat similar to the one to be stationed at Whitby from 1988.

5. Salmon and Trout

At the begining of this book I suggested that there might have been friction between the indigenous population and the abbey over the fishing; this is borne out when you read T.H. English's book on the *Yorkshire Esk Fishery Association* to which I am indebted for historical information on the salmon and trout fishery in the river. But the first record he gives is from 1200 when the monastery of the Benedictine order had been established in the new buildings arising after William the Conqueror.

The fishery rights were given "to a Convent of Monks from Normandy giving them the whole reach of the river that they may have free and undisturbed fishing, and may exercise fishing rights in the whole reach of the river, and that no-one may enter below their boundary for the purpose of fishing." In later years their rights were "let" for annual payments, particularly to those who had grinding mills worked by water power, and in the reign of Charles I (1625) there was a long legal dispute about making "Hecks" on the river – which were fish traps to catch fish coming up the river on their migration from the sea.

"There were several of these traps on the river. As late as 1863 there was one at Ruswarp, three miles upstream from the mouth, for the use of which the mill paid £50 a year. The dam was made of rough stones and branches (so Mr Swales, the old cobbler of Sleights, told me) with a pass in it, in which a bag net was set looking up stream and weighted with stones. Each season they built a little hut hard by in which they used to sit and play cards and have a sup in nights of flood, when the fish were coming up, going out every half hour and lifting the end of the net to see if a fish were in it . . . how any fish survived this continual persecution is difficult to understand, except that in very big floods they managed to evade the traps more easily . . ."

Presumably there were also those who paid no dues and tickled under the stones in the gipsy manner; how many fish were caught and how many survived can only be conjectured but Sir Walter Scott in 1821, "who evidently knew the Esk as a salmon river", writes of one of his characters (they lived on the banks of the Esk) . . . "to escape the daily necessity of eating salmon whether in or out of season six days out of the seven" – which presumably was somewhat poetic licence particularly in pre-refrigerator days.

But was it salmon? From reading and re-reading the books and documents I am very sure that what they were catching was sea trout – otherwise known as salmon trout or bull-trout – and it was only after the beginnings of the Esk Fishery Association in 1864 and their importing and hatching of salmon eggs from other rivers that the Esk became a salmon river. There were plenty of trout according to a letter in the *Whitby Gazette* stating that 560 lbs weight of salmon trout "had been taken in nets in and near Ruswarp within the last fortnight",

The salmon and trout hatchery at Glaisdale: Netting young fish from the holding pool ready for transfer to the upper reaches of the river Esk (opposite, top). Separating young fish after netting them in the holding pool (opposite, bottom). Dave Cook, water bailiff, taking off infertile eggs from the hatching troughs (above, left). Young fish ready for transfer to the streamlets in the upper reaches of the river Esk (above, right). In the 1980s fish were sent to the river Tees as it became less polluted, returning the compliment for stock sent from the Tees to the Esk in the 1800s when Esk stock was virtually nil. Salmon return to the river in which they grew and those that went to the Tees would return there.

presumably at the licensed mill trap for the letter goes on, "and this at a time when the law imposes a severe penalty upon everyone in possession of a salmon, as may be seen in a report of the *Whitby Times* of Monday week when a man, for being in possession of a salmon was fined £3 and costs."

The local Association having been formed with many local notabilities on the committee – who funded it with subscriptions of £10 apiece – members' tickets were introduced to allow fishing in the club waters. These waters were (a) the whole length of the Esk proper and (b) the whole of Goathland Beck. The landowners along the river appeared to have generally consented to the arrangement and received a couple of membership tickets apiece to fish in their own territory but not those adjoining without permission. As might be expected there were howls of indignation from those who had formerly fished where they liked. The *Whitby Times* of March 23rd, 1866 printed a letter protesting "at taking away the rights of the people and disenfranchising them of the sport of piscation without being compelled to apply to Tavern Landlords or jerry lords for a licence to do so." However the Association went on and made a decision to obtain proper salmon ova from the river Tees. This was done in 1864, the eggs hatched in a rainwater butt at

Egton Bridge, the young fish put in the river and the first salmon caught in 1872 by a clergyman, Rev Philpot, at Half Crown Pool alongside the old toll road from Grosmont to Egton Bridge. Two more were caught before the year was out. In 1874 three were caught in the Associations' water but "thousands were caught both at sea and in the river, increasing the revenue of Whitby sea-fishermen by leaps and bounds".

H.T. English's book says, "The tremendous success of this venture in spite of its difficulties makes one glad that its authors lived to see the thousands of pounds that their action annually adds to the funds of the present sea fishermen of Whitby and the enviable position in which the little river Esk now stands as a salmon stream. Our thanks to the Tees should never be forgotten and maybe the day will come when, owing to present pollution there, we may be able to repay their kindness." That was written in 1925 and in the intervening years the chemical conurbation around the Tees grew and the pollution became impossible for any fish. But opinions changed, clean-up operations began and by the late 1970s enough had been done for the Esk Fishery Association to be called upon to repay, and salmon ova were returned from the Esk to the Tees.

Weirs and fish ladders were instituted or repaired by the Association in conjunction with the Esk Board of Conservators who were the authority in charge of the river (authority later under the Yorkshire Ouse River Board and now the Yorkshire Water Authority), whose licence to fish in the river was – and is – still required before members could even fish in their own waters adjoining their land. The requirement of hatching resulted eventually in the building of a permanent hatchery at Glaisdale by the Egton Estates Company capable of hatching out 100,000 fish at a time. This is still in use and in 1987 50,000 eggs were bought from Scottish sources, paid for equally by the Esk Fishery Association, the Water

Authority and the Whitby Coble Fisherman's Association who have assisted with the cost for the last three years. The young fish are put into streams in the upper reaches of the Esk in late April after the water has been cleared of salmon trout who would have a banquet. (The trout are electrically stunned and returned to the main stretches of the river). Even so it is estimated that only 5% will ever return as adult fish. The fact that the adult fish, hatched from the imported eggs, return to the Esk is put down to the fact that it is the first river that they get the smell of after hatching.

Before leaving these upper waters of the Esk to expand on the activities around the mouth, I must quote the preface to Mr English's book:

> Oh! most divinely beautiful lady, my lady of the Esk, thou knowest it is no exaggeration for me to say that I have loved thee and worshipped at thy shrine all my life, with the ardour of an ancient Briton's reverence for his rover's goddess; in fact, some say that I have almost lived for thee and thee alone and why not? Though my hair is now white, is not thy marvellous beauty as fresh as ever, as each springtime touches thy cheek, and is there aught that I love more than to wander among the primroses and daffodils by thy side, listening to thy sweet song in every run, to the accompanying notes of blackbird and thrush, as a soft south-west wind bears fresh scents across thy woods and meadows?

An idyllic picture – surely true for most of the time but in contrast to a story he tells of a clergyman caught fishing with worms instead of flies and an irate purist throwing stones in the water to spoil his fishing!

Sea fishing off the mouth of the Esk in 1886 was confined by licences to local men and was done with nets six to eight feet deep with a two-inch mesh; in about 1889 Hartlepool fishermen got licences and fished the Whitby

Opposite
The dam across the river Esk at Ruswarp has a salmon ladder but in 1964 the drought was so severe that water bailiff Louis Nelmes spent hours helping the fish on their way up river to spawn.

Above
Drying salmon nets in front of the Duke of York hotel on the east side of the lower harbour.

Opposite
The car in the background gives the era; net mending has decreased with the use of man-made instead of natural fibres but a seal, a shark or a mine can still cause damage – and loss of fish.

district using nets thirty feet deep with a larger mesh of 5½ to 6 inches and caught larger fish, soon adopted by the Whitby men. The season was from May to August 31st. Now it is for salmon from the first of February, and for trout from the first of March, until the end of August, although it is normally April before the boats go out and often not until mid-May.

A fleet of about twenty cobles go out from Whitby and others from Staithes, ten miles further north; the area they are licensed to fish extends south to the Humber but the practical area probably goes no further than eight miles south of Whitby. The Whitby and Staithes Coblemen's Association contribute, as has been said, to the £1,800 cost of re-stocking the river each year; they appreciate what has been done over the years and want to help, but comment that it is a losing battle with poachers in the river; however, one cobleman remarked that there were still plenty of salmon in the upper reaches last November – they had been

to have a look "and you could have walked across the river on their backs." The percentage that do get back to the breeding grounds in the upper Esk will provide thousands of eggs so it must be a worthwhile exercise. The salmon poachers work in the lower reaches with nets, but higher up it is torches and gaffs on the breeding beds. "That's where they were getting them last November and some of them had freezers full. Many of them are in pretty poor condition but people who buy from them from West Yorkshire and Teesside don't mind – they get them at a cheap price and serve them up in restaurants." He went on to say that the best salmon were those that were "fresh run" in the early part of the season until August; "you can tell, if they have lice on them they're fresh run but if they're clean they've been around for a while. They get a bit black round the scales.

Opposite
1960 and a salmon net to repair.

Below
The local fishing industry is still labour-intensive; the boxes of fish are individually weighed and tallied – and this at six o'clock in the morning after a night's fishing.

"They come in on a tide; you can go out and there's nothing, and then suddenly there's plenty. But for what we take with four hundred yards of net there must be thousands go past out at sea. The nets are all monofilament with five-inch mesh, twenty-five feet deep, with a cork line at the top and lead line at the bottom and they just drift. Anything under three or four pounds gets out – we don't want to be doing what the Danes and Germans are doing, cleaning out the lot. You want some to be going forward and small fish can lay as many eggs as bigger ones. We might get twenty salmon in a day, average ten to twelve pounds apiece with a few up to twenty pounds weight. The price we get has gone down; in 1976 salmon was bringing £2 a pound, in 1986 £1.60. Salmon used to be the cream of your catch but the price of cod now is even better. When you buy a salmon there's less waste than there is on a cod – you probably only lose ten per cent when you dress them."

Regulations permit salmon fishing between 4 a.m. and 8 p.m. but finishing at 6 p.m. on Friday until 6 a.m. Monday morning. Salmoning used to be a mainly night-time operation, but that has changed because of the number of seals. "When we were laid alongside the nets at night we could hear the fish going in but we couldn't find them – the seals had got them. You could drive a bus through the holes in the nets. The seal problem has become worse, there were eighteen in one area of 150 yards last year. You can shoot them but they seem to know – they hang around on the shore side, and no one in their right minds would use a high-powered rifle towards the beach."

What do these seals look like – are they like the bundles of fur we see on television being slaughtered in Canada?

"They look like something out of Spielburg's horror movies; they weigh about a ton, look rather like a walrus, bigger than a sea lion; they have great rolls of fat around their necks covered in sores and lice, and if you're down wind of them you can smell them a mile away. They leave large oily patches on top of the water, and the smell is like rotting seaweed. They do wanton damage, take one bite out of a fish, kill it and grab another one. Nowadays its not just salmon, they were attacking our lines last winter; we were hauling a line aboard and a seal came and took more than thirty fish, about ten stone weight. In the herring season they hang around as the nets are hauled and take the fish that fall out – they're bone lazy. Believe me, these are not Walt Disney characters!" An interesting theory was put forward by a retired fisherman who served in minesweepers during the last war. He said, "The minesweepers were fitted with Asdic, which gave a 'ping' whenever something solid and of some size was detected under water, and a mine was immediately dropped overboard. The result was that many killer whales, who until then had kept down the seal population, were themselves killed."

Robert Peart said, "In all the years I've been fishing I've only once seen tunny; that was three years ago three-quarters of a mile off Ness End, Robin Hood's Bay. There were big beds of sprat and herring in late July and the tunny were diving and jumping through them. They were big, a metallic grey and with a forked tail like a mackerel."

If you discuss salmon and trout fishing with the experts of the Yorkshire Water Authority, they were happier in the days when poachers were a traditional breed who played a game that was known to them and the water bailiffs – and examples were made now and then to keep things in check. Nowadays it's big business with groups and gangs descending on the river at night, bailiffs assaulted, suspicions that there are firearms and crossbows ready for use and stone throwing a regular occurrence. A bye-law has been brought into operation in 1987, to be reviewed after ten years, which forbids any fishing for salmon and trout in the tidal reaches of the Esk as far up as Ruswarp Bridge; this has brought forth strong objections from those who traditionally fished there but the Water Authority see it as the only way to deal with "snatching" the fish in an area where they are completely vulnerable, and there have been many nights when this length of river has been criss-crossed by so many nets that nothing could pass.

6. Herrings – the silver darlings

The abbots, we know, had herring stored in their kitchens in 1394. As has been recounted, in that year great shoals arrived which attracted buyers who sold the herring for export until there were not enough left to feed the local population. The shoals must have been visiting the north-east coast long before then. We know that herring curing houses were built in 1833 at Tate Hill which presupposes a worthwhile trade. Our knowledge of the late nineteenth and first half of the twentieth centuries is detailed and explicit – but methods apart from mechanisation can have changed little. What will never come back is the scene reported on September 29th, 1897 when so great was the catch that barrels filled the New Quay, the pavements above and below the bridge, and four long trains, each with two steam engines, left Whitby in the one day.

The herring *(family Clupea)* is not confined to the North Sea – there is a species in the Pacific which is caught both on the Asiatic and American coasts, there are others up in the Arctic, and it seems that the further north the larger the fish. "An immature fish from the Norwegian coast can be much bigger than a mature fish from the Southern North Sea." Even the North Sea herrings can be divided into different tribes which spawn at slightly different times." Spring breaks out in the sea just as it does in the fields, woods and hedgerows on shore. The small marine animals – the plankton – on which the herring feed are beginning to swarm in May and the fish, after a winter of starvation, start to aggregate on the patches of plankton. The great feeding season is beginning" – according to a book *The Herring and its Fishery* written by Dr W. Hodgson, from which this author is grateful for some technical details. "The feeding season reaches its peak in June and this, naturally, is accompanied by a wonderful increase in the quality of the fish." By August the whole of the central North Sea, from the Shetlands to the north Yorkshire coast, became a fishing ground for excellent quality herrings. Writings of the period up to 1955, when there was a catastrophic decline in the industry, Dr Hodgson comments that by September the Yorkshire fishery was at its height. By October the shoals had moved south, heading for the banks off the north French and Belgian coasts.

Herring fishing at Whitby had been carried on for many years by local boats but in the late nineteenth century they were joined by Penzancemen – a term which included boats from Penzance, St. Ives, Newlyn, Mousehole, Fowey, and other ports in Cornwall, plus boats from Lowestoft and Yarmouth as well as Peel in the Isle of Man. An eye-witness account appeared in the *Whitby Gazette* when a correspondent recalled that "it would be June 1875 when, one Saturday afternoon I was taken for a sail in a pointed-stern coble by John Douglas, and whilst we were out about forty Cornish boats arrived at Whitby." He and another writer agreed that the first to arrive was the *White Star* owned and crewed by five Jackson brothers. "She was a boat of some twenty tons, she had a round stern and very fine lines and was a fast sailer. Like all the other Cornish vessels she had two masts and carried two lug sails and a gaff-topsail; very occasionally a jib was set." Two years later the Jacksons had a new boat, the *Colleen Bawn*, the first pointed-sterned Cornish boat to visit Whitby.

In addition to these, there were the Staithes

The Scottish fisher lasses gipping herring on the quay were an annual sight, reputedly with a slickness of hand which defied belief. Very few photographs survive of activities in the early years of this century. The buildings in the background remain much the same – but the Nelson's Flag Inn is part of an amusement arcade . . .

yawls – or "yackers" – which were "larger and stouter craft all built at Whitby, owned in Staithes and registered in Whitby". There were also the local mules, and the "ploshers" as the cobles were called. The big Staithes craft and sometimes a few of the Cornish boats ventured to the off-ground fishing, some sixty miles off, putting down their fish in salt and remaining at sea for some days, but the rest worked grounds from three to seven miles off. The fleet anchored daily in the roadstead off the harbour until it was time to sail for the night's fishing – the skippers were quite content to know there was a port to which they could run for shelter if necessary, only coming into harbour at weekends. "In the dark the boats presented a very attractive sight, with their riding lights stretching across the horizon from the extreme north to the extreme south."

The first boat back would be one of those known as "pole-enders" described as men of no great reputation; "they might get their nets wet but got herring by going to the end farthest away from the large fishing boats, and then shook the net across their boat. When they had satisfied themselves with the fish thus obtained they ran to port, reached the market first, and always got top prices."

The rest of the fleet came in the following morning to discharge their catch – if the tide was out they occasionally landed them on the sands using their "punts", the small dinghys that all the boats carried. An army of buyers' agents waited at the market on the pier, a sample basket of herring from each boat was turned out to be bid for, and then the landing began. Cargoes were discharged at the quay above the bridge: from Collier's Ghaut to the far end of the quay where a flight of wooden steps led up to the railway station the area was divided up into sections for the different buyers, each with tiers of barrels "packed to a great height". On days of great landings the area would stretch down St. Ann's Staith below the bridge – but there was not the quay beyond Haggersgate as there is now.

In both areas would be the Scottish fisher lasses; to quote Dr Hodgson's book, "It used to be a great attraction watching the girls and admiring the skill with which they yielded the short gutting knife, making an incision in the throat of the fish and withdrawing the gill and long gut in one neat stroke." For how many years these girls had been following the herring boats down the coast is not recorded, but Dr Hodgson states that it was in the fourteenth century that a Dutchman changed the system from merely packing the complete fish in salt in barrels to gutting or "gipping" them. Certainly one of Whitby's sights in the early days of this century was these Scottish girls, dressed in brightly coloured woollen jumpers, thick skirts, heavy leather half-wellingtons, oily aprons and woollen shawls, standing over the troughs of herring and seemingly effortlessly gipping and slipping the fish into baskets. They worked in teams of three, two gipping and one packing them into the baskets – and sorting them into three sizes as they did so.

The herrings were sold in hundreds, with ten thousand to the "last". The counting was done by taking a couple of herring in each hand, and as each four fish, called a "warp", was deposited, "one, two, three, etc" was shouted until the "thirty" was reached; another warp was added, when the teller shouted "tally". Thus, in fact, there were 124 fish to the hundred. It was at a later date that herring were sold by the "cran". In counting the herrings a record or tally was kept with chalk on a board, a stroke was made for each hundred, and after four strokes a diagonal line was drawn across – which counted as 500, or actually 620, in a basket.

The packing of the fish into barrels was carried out by men, some of whom tipped the baskets whilst others sprinkled in rough salt, or ice. When the barrel was filled, paper, straw or sackcloth provided a covering which was then fastened with a hoop. Then the rush for the railway station began, "with much congestion and confusion on the road".

Meantime the boats had returned to anchor off the harbour mouth except at weekends; the harbour presented a forest of masts and it is said that, above the bridge, a man was once able to walk across the tiers of boats from one side of the harbour to the other. The nets of many of the boats were transferred to carts, piled up like a load of hay and taken to a field to spread out to dry, whilst others suspended their nets on a pole high above the deck and extending across between the two masts. Others took their nets for treatment to the barking coppers – the cotton nets needed to be treated against bacterial action and the usual method was to soak them in a solution of cutch, a process known as barking. The arrival of the boats – and their departure on Monday – caused great inconvenience to passengers across the bridge, which stayed open for half an hour at a time, a slow process because bridge dues were collected from each boat by means of a very long pole at the end of which was a pocket into which the man on board the boat dropped the requisite coins. Saturday was also a busy day for shopping with two of the crew carrying a herring basket which they filled with bread loaves, potatoes and other vegetables especially cabbage. "In a large number of cases, on top of the basket would be one or more of 'Coles Cheesecakes' – a favourite delicacy among the fishermen. It was the size of a good sized plate, about one and a half inches deep and filled with curds. The price was only twopence and they were made by William Cole whose bakery was at the east end of the swing bridge." The sliced cabbage was used in a meat soup which was a staple of their diet, together with a raisin and suet pudding known as "plum duff". "A favourite meal at sea was herring, cooked in a deep pan, and eaten with hard cabin biscuit broken into a basin of boiling hot tea."

The Cornishmen as a rule were very religious, more so than some of the men from other areas. Every boat had a name flag floating from the masthead on Sunday morning and very often a service was held on one of the boats, the Missions to Seamen flag being hoisted and the reader taking his portable harmonium. Crowds gathered on the quayside to listen to the singing. A number of the Cornishmen took Sunday afternoon service in one of the village chapels and "they were vehement in their audible ejaculations of Hallelujah, Praise the Lord and such like punctuations during the prayers".

"An incident worth recording occurred during the height of one fishing season. For some unaccountable reason the herring seemed to have left the coast and for many days the boats returned to port without a catch. Matters became so serious that the men were unable to send any money to their homes, and some boats actually remained in harbour deeming it not worth while to go to sea. Eventually some of the Cornishmen decided to hold a prayer meeting in the Old Primitive Methodist Chapel in Church Street to pray for fish. It is a remarkable fact that when next the boats went fishing they secured abnormal catches. I can vividly recall the incident", said Mr F. W. Horne, "for I attended the service referred to. I recollect the amazement with which I watched boat after boat, laden with herring, come into the harbour." By the end of September the boats had all left, heading down the coast and eventually to home ports for the winter.

From 1897 the number of Cornish vessels visiting Whitby gradually decreased to around twenty, although boats from Berwick, Newbiggin, Blyth and Hartlepool were coming to work alongside Whitby craft. There had been some poor seasons, but it is said that the moving of one of the main buyers to Scarborough due to pressure from insurers was a main reason. "Though the Cornishmen liked Whitby best, they had to conform to the rulings of the insurers."

In 1908 work commenced on building the extensions to the piers and a wooden quay was built alongside the pier above the Scotch Head, all completed before 1914 when the war started and many boats were pressed into service. There was a small flutter of activity for a couple of years after the war with herring drifters but they found it better to work out of Yarmouth.

Tunny Fishing

The local fleet continued, in season, to catch the herrings as they came south, and in 1932 a new sideline occurred when Mr L. Mitchell-Henry, a big fish angler, commissioned the Whitby boat *Fortunatus* (Skipper Matthew Leadley) as his depot ship for the North Sea tunny fishing season.

The tunny (thunnus thynnus), so the records say, was hunted by the Romans who ate it either fresh or salted; its name derives from the Greek signifying great rapidity of flight. One of the family was caught two miles off Whitby in a herring net on September 9th, 1882, and part of it is "set up" in Whitby Museum. But the giant fish had rarely been seen off the Yorkshire coast until the 1930s, probably because no-one was particularly interested until Mr Mitchell-Henry and his partner Mr F.B. Hannam, vice chairman of the British Sea Anglers' Society, arrived. He opined that Whitby was an ideal centre for the sport; they had implicit confidence in the *Fortunatus* and its crew, and Whitby was near to the herring grounds where tunny were to be found sporting themselves. "The reason why they stay off Whitby and do not go much further to the south is that they prefer a clean and sandy bottom," he said.

Whatever the reason, the departure of the boat for the first hunt aroused a degree of local anticipation according to a report in the *Whitby Gazette* for August 26th, 1932, and I quote verbatim:

Opposite
A Fishing Harvest Festival was held in the Primitive Methodist Church, Church Street, Whitby, in the years of the herring glut. The church is now a warehouse.

Return of the *Fortunatus*

Towards noon a little knot of the more enthusiastic admirers of the intrepid tunny fighters gathered at the end of the West Pier extension for the arrival of any boat bringing news of the whereabouts of the *Fortunatus*. Almost on the stroke of noon a boat was seen coming through the haze and expectancy reached a high pitch when it was recognised as Mr Mitchell-Henry's craft. When something was seen to be hoisted on the mizzen there wee excited whisperings, as it had been arranged that if a tunny was caught a flag would be hoisted as a signal. Still, it was not certain and as the tide was out the anchor was dropped off the West Pier extension end.

It was not long before a foy boat came alongside and the members of the crew were being rowed up the harbour. Answering a signal from the West Pier, those in the boat indicated that Mr Mitchell-Henry had caught a tunny and that 'it was a big 'un'. People on the harbourside seemed to anticipate the news which spread through the town like wildfire. By the time the boat reached the landing steps there was a large crowd eager to share by their presence in congratulating him. Although mainfestly tired after being on the move for twenty-nine-and-a-half hours during five of which he had been engaged in a gruelling fight with one of the gamest of big fishes, Mr Mitchell-Henry was obviously happy and to one of those who offered congratulations he emphasised that he was pleased to have fulfilled his promise to land a tunny at Whitby so soon. The crew did not disguise their delight and admiration of him as a great angler. The estimate of the weight of the fish was round about seven hundred pounds, an estimate which proved singularly correct. By half past two the water had risen sufficiently to enable the craft to creep slowly up the channel to the Fish Quay where thousands of people had taken their stand in the hope of seeing the monster.

The tale of the hunt followed: the *Fortunatus* had left port at seven a.m. shaping a north-easterly course – straight out from the extensions – for the herring grounds. By nightfall they came up with some drifters who confirmed they had seen tunny not far away:

A smart lookout was rewarded by two tunny being seen sporting near a herring shoal, sometimes darting in amongst them in characteristic fashion. By this time night had fallen, the sea was becoming jowly which seemed to whet the appetite of the tunny for they began to take the herring greedily. Mr Mitchell-Henry decided to turn in for a rest whilst Skipper Leadley judiciously fed the tunny with herrings which were taken with eagerness. Eventually they swam quite close to the *Fortunatus*, snapping at the herrings before they had floated far away.

Mr Mitchell-Henry came on deck:

"He saw that the hour he had been waiting for had arrived, and that there was a good chance of hooking what promised to be a tunny that would give him a good fight. Despite the fact that the night was dark and the sea had risen considerably, he and one of the boatmen were soon in the little rowing boat – it is one of the most stringent rules of the game that tunny shall be hooked from a rowing boat, and not taken from a power boat. In the meantime the tunny were induced to keep near the surface by herring thrown overboard from the Fortunatus. The rowing boat sheered off and Mr Mitchell-Henry launched a herring on a hook. Very soon the sudden and high pitched whirr of the reel, as scores of yards of line went out in an incredibly short space of time, proclaimed the indisputable fact that something big had taken the bait and the hook.

Then came a duel which took the form of a battle royal between a monster fish and an expert angler. There was no mistaking the fact that the tunny was as determined to regain its freedom as Mr Mitchell-Henry was that the line should remain intact. It was half-past midnight when the tunny took the hook. The way the fish dived and

The herring fleet was an attraction for the late summer holiday makers, but did they realise the implications of the multitudes of herring being shovelled into barrels to be sent for pet food, or fertiliser manufacture, or ploughing into the ground?

rose, whisked about and then made off in a mad rush, was thrilling in the extreme. Those on the *Fortunatus* realised the odds against the angler. One false move and the fish would be lost and the boat possibly capsized. The fish was in its own element and weighed considerably more than the rowing boat and its occupants.

Sometimes the boat was towed in a straight line and at others in a circle, and this went on for four hours in the darkness. At half-past four there was sufficient light to see that Mr Mitchell-Henry was wearing down his catch but it took a further hour before he could claim the victory. The fight ended a little over twelve miles from where it began.

After exhibition on the quay at Whitby, where £10 was raised for charity, the fish was taken to Leeds market where it was sold for tenpence a pound "any cut". Mr Mitchell-Henry continued hunting from Whitby the following year and then moved to Scarborough. The only tunny fishing today is, I understand, off the American coast; in this country, like hunting and other activities, there seems a feeling against all killing for sport.

The Second War lets the Herring multiply

Apart from small catches by local boats there was no major activity until after the Second World War. During that war most of the

Above

An impressive line-up of local and Scottish boats, bow-on to the quay; imagine them laid side by side and you may believe that it was possible to walk across the decks from one side of the harbour to the other. This was reputedly possible at the turn of the century, and Mrs Ann Leadley says that in the 1950s on Sunday mornings she carried Yorkshire Puddings and a jug of gravy from the east side where she lived across to a boat skippered by a Scottish friend of the family.

Left

Fewer of the herring fleet were to be found in the lower harbour on the Sunday in September when the Blessing of the Boats service was held – after a week at sea the crews needed their siesta!

In the immediate post war years, when food was generally scarce but herring was in abundance, residents of villages in the area offered to send a lorry to collect supplies – at normal prices – but it is alleged that the bureaucracy couldn't accommodate the activity, so the fish went for fertiliser.

fishermen had gone into the Royal Naval Reserve and, with many of the boats, were engaged in minesweeping. The older men and younger boys under eighteen were all that were left to bring in what fish they could as part of the wartime diet. One authority has stated that the two wars saved the fishing industry; prior to the First War catches were poor as they were before the Second War. Virtually left in peace the fish multiplied – and especially the herring, regarded by the local men as the cream of their crop where they made the most

money. The men came back from the forces with their gratuities, the white fish subsidy helped with the building of new boats – and caused the re-opening of the Whitehall Shipyard to build keel boats and seine-netters – and the first herring fishing season was in 1946. It started slowly but as word spread of the tremendous shoals of herring, the following year many more boats were busy and they were joined by many Scottish boats, both ring-netters and drifters, a total of 130 boats fishing out of Whitby and including probably about

twenty Whitby keelboats. Large Dutch drifters and Polish boats were there, mostly packing their catch in barrels to take back with them – mobile factories, catering for their national liking for eating raw herring. The Scottish and local boats' catches were watched over by a Herring Industry Board official who reported daily to the Ministry of Food in London, and daily quotas for catches were set for which a price was imposed. There was such a glut that after quota quantities had been fulfilled millions of herrings went for the manufacture of fertiliser and for animal feed. There were even days when the fertiliser industry had enough and the fish were dumped back at sea.

This caused much ill-feeling in the area; food was still rationed, there was a Food Office in the town. People in the surrounding villages got together and offered to send a van at their own expense to collect herrings – and pay for them – but the Ministry refused. The chairman of the Whitby Food Committee was George Lyth, a farmer from Lealholm, a blunt man who made a strong case at their meetings, but the Man from the Ministry insisted that they could not deal with small quantities, it must all be controlled. By 1954 the catch was diminishing; Russian and Dutch Factory ships moved in and, using methods akin to Hoovering, took young fish as well as adults deliberately wherever they could find large shoals. German "Arctic type" trawlers came in such large numbers that smaller boats could not find room to work. They were "towing gear at over 15 knots, catching large bags of herrings and, said a skipper, leaving a trail of dead herring and haddocks

Left
So many boats were hunting the herring that occasionally nets were tangled. This incident, when the author was on board the "Success", took from midnight until 11.00 the following morning to sort out.

Right
John James Storr on board "Provider" in August 1963, with a few words to say about a bit of a tangle.

behind them, which made him think that they were catching fish at a greater rate than they could stow them in the holds".

The practical reason for the increase in the herring catch was due, to a great extent, to the invention of the Echometer which gave a trace on paper in the boat's wheelhouse when the shoals were underneath. Up to that time drift nets had been thrown over at places where the skipper hoped his experience would find the fish, whilst with the Echometer it was possible to use ring nets – either from one boat or more efficiently working in pairs – to encircle the shoal.

Three things ensued – even bigger nets were used, the horsepower of the boats increased and a market opened up for fish meal which meant that whilst previously there

was finite market, after which extra quantities could not be absorbed, this new outlet meant an unlimited demand, possibly not at top prices but still at an economic level. A gentleman's agreement between the local and Scottish fishermen not to sell for fishmeal and so maintain the market price existed for a while, and some skippers dumped excess catches at sea rather than flood the market, but there was no general support. Fertiliser factories had existed for some years but had only taken poor quality fish and offal – but there had not been a specific fishery for their requirements.

A ban came into force stopping fishing in the spawning grounds on the North Yorkshire and Northumberland coasts in 1975 but it continued in the eastern North Sea off the

Above

In 1959 when herrings were falling off the backs of lorries, so many were there, these lads set up a stall on the fish quay selling at one penny a fish. They even had a regular contract with an old lady for a daily supply for her cat.

Opposite

So great was the interest by visitors to see the fleet depart that a notice board on the quay was chalked up with the time, each evening. On the east cliff a retired fisherman and his family sit on the grass thinking of times past – and times, perhaps, to come.

Danish Coast and the Skaggerrak. The Yorkshire fishermen complained bitterly over the next nine years because the ban in their area had led to no improvement in stocks; eventually the eastern North Sea was put under the ban and within two years the herring were back. According to a man with a lifelong experience, the herring were spawning off the north-east coast and spent their juvenile life in the shallow waters near the Danish coast and the Skaggerak before returning eighteen months later. Stocks in the North Sea are probably at their best since the mid 1960s but the Yorkshire coast ban still remains for the period from August 14th to the end of September – to protect the breeding stocks – the very time when they are in economic quantities for the local boats to catch. There

smoked millions of them, starting just after the First World War. The kippers, nowadays, are made from Icelandic herring, until the North Sea supplies are freely available again; they are cut down the back, gutted, washed, soaked in brine for half an hour, and then smoked for ten to twelve hours. The shavings light the sawdust, and the sawdust stops the shavings from bursting into flame; the herring are hung high in the roof so they can't burn.

Many Whitby Kippers used to be sent off by post but high postal charges have virtually stopped it. All the weekly production of around 2,500 pairs in summer, and 800 in winter, is sold straight from the Fortune's shop in Henrietta Street and other outlets in the town.

Nine Days Wonder

Early one misty morning at the height of the herring season in September 1954 a dirty, battered-looking Polish boat *Puszchik* came into the harbour. Skipper John James Storr of the Whitby boat *Provider* had been hailed at sea by a crew member of the Polish boat, had gone aboard and in spite of language difficulties had understood that they wanted to come into the port. It was 5 a.m. when the little convoy came through the harbour mouth and it was then that the drama started. There had been a mutiny.

Members of the crew had seen the Political Officer making notes of their "subversive" conversations with the obvious intention of reporting them to his masters. When the captain went to the ship's toilet they locked him in, telling him that they had nothing against him. They then went after the Political Officer with the intention of his falling over the side "accidentally". They broke into his cabin and in the struggle that followed he received a head wound but managed to throw them out. He barricaded himself in and made a fearsome "cosh" out of part of his bunk wrapped round with wire.

It was then that the mutineers decided to give themselves up and headed the ship for Whitby and came into port with the Political Officer still barricaded in his cabin and ignorant even of what port he was in. It took some time for the Whitby police to persuade him to come out – and they were under the impression that he had a revolver.

The seven mutineers came ashore and asked the Harbour master, Captain Frank Graves, for political asylum, and they were placed under police guard in his office. The remainder of the crew, who were married men and feared what would happen to their families back home, remained on board. The captain was freed.

At 7 a.m. the author of this book received a mysterious phone call suggesting he brought his camera to the Harbour Office. He was greeted by Captain Graves who outlined the story and said the men were under police guard in the main office.

I went along a corridor, turned into the doorway on the left and saw the mutineers sitting in chairs around the window at the far end. A policeman was between me and them, sitting over the fire, knees up the chimney, fast asleep and remained oblivious to the fact that I had taken a photograph. I left the office, went across Pier Road to the quayside and was busy taking some shots of the ship when a police inspector arrived, greeted me and hoped that I had some interesting pictures – which I assured him I had without giving details. I went back to the darkroom, developed and printed the film, sent prints off by three taxis in three directions and went home for breakfast. At about eleven o'clock the police inspector phoned – someone had talked! He said that the matter was sub judice, that the Home Office was involved, and I must not send photographs to the press.

With my helpful co-operation, half an hour later he had found out that a picture had gone to the *Yorkshire Evening Post* and that they had already published it in an early edition; the cat was out of the bag! The pictures were used

Opposite
The "Puszchik" in Whitby harbour.

Above
The seven Polish seamen who mutinied, seen in the Harbour Master's office shortly after they came ashore.

Opposite
The Political Officer after his release from a cabin where the mutineers had imprisoned him.

all over the world, the only real scoop I ever had. Whether it was worth the hassle of the next couple of years of being moved on for parking, almost for breathing in a public place, I don't know.

It was literally a nine days wonder, there are very few stories that stay on the front page of newspapers for that length of time; the mutineers had asked for political asylum, the Polish Ambassador strenuously opposed it, and it developed into a High Court case. The

reason for the mutiny became more obvious – conditions on board these ships were bad, they worked very long hours in what was a nationalised industry. No matter how good the catch was they were still paid the same pittance whilst the Scottish and Whitby men they saw in port had better conditions and made more money whilst they couldn't afford a nip of vodka.

Meanwhile the *Puszchik* laid in Whitby harbour in a prominent position alongside St.

Ann's Staith – its original berth had been where the herring fleet moored. There were quite a few visitors still in the town and there were large crowds along the quay. The Commissar strolled around the deck and revelled in the attention. He was a swarthy man with a moustache, still wearing the blood-stained bandage round his head and very ready to give any girls the eye. The skipper was still on board but keeping out of sight – he was probably very sure that there would be a black mark on his record. Representatives of the "Free Poland Society" arrived in town, an organisation devoted to freeing the country from Communist rule, with a large flamboyant lady as their spokesman; from the quayside she tried to persuade the remainder of the crew to come ashore. "Join your brothers in England, the land of the free!" she shouted, and the Commissar shouted back, obscenities were exchanged which ended with the lady suggesting the mutineers should have cut his head off whilst they were about it. He responded by jumping up and down, which was marvellous material for the reporters and photographers. Eventually the court case was completed, asylum was granted, and every one of the men departed for America! Some years later the skipper returned to the port, visited the Duke of York Inn and presented them with a tunny fish tail mounted in a cabinet with an inscription from Captain Wiktor Cobryn.

Shipbuilding

Opposite, top
Mr Jack Lowther opened a yard to build cobles and half-size seine netters at Spital Bridge, a stream off the river Esk in the upper harbour; the yard is still working. The stream had been dammed off as a timber pond in the 1750s, and on the land running alongside was one of the town's three roperies. There is a tight limit on the depth of vessel Mr Lowther can build due to two low bridges between his yard and the main river, and a fine line of judgement is required to judge the height of the tide and the draught of the vessel.

Opposite, bottom
Half-size seine netters were fashionable for a few years, and were built at Jack Lowther's yard at Spital Bridge.

After the end of the second World War the Whitehall Shipyard re-opened in the upper harbour on a site covering seven acres. The yard had been in use from the 1750s and, under various owners, produced wood sailing ships, iron ships with sails and motors, and concrete hulls in wartime. The 1946 re-opening was enabled by the White Fish Subsidy Act intended to replace boats lost during the war when they had been commandeered for mine sweeping and for the Dunkirk evacuation. Facilities at the yard were rudimentary and building at first took place outdoors with methods presumably not much different from two hundred years before. The picture (opposite) shows the schooner "Gratitude" which had been laid up in the harbour during the war years and which was the first to be refurbished when the yard re-opened.

Early post war years at Whitehall Shipyard, before there was a building shed in use; the picture (above) shows the frames of the first seine netter to be built.

Bending on a plank at Goodall's yard at Sandsend; this coble built in 1987 complete with engine, echo sounder, power winch and modern necessities worked out at £1,000 a foot; in the 1920s and '30s a basic coble cost £1 a foot. In 1780 the going rate for a 20ft long coble, three pairs of oars, rudder, anchor, and six fathoms of anchor chain was £8.50.

Never two the same – from the 1750s it was practice to find a tree somewhere near the shape for the stem. In those days there were no drawings or plans – it was rule of thumb and experience. In the 1950s there were plans but still a tree of the right shape was a major bonus.

7. The Cod Quota

The European Economic Community (EEC) has ruled that the amount of cod caught in the North Sea shall be limited to a specific weight of gutted fish per crewman per week; at the date of writing, May 1987, the amount is twenty-one boxes each of eight stone per man per week and this figure can fluctuate as decreed each month. Most of the eighteen Whitby boats have a crew of four, one or two carrying five or six. Skippers must keep a daily record of catches, and these log sheets are sent, for this area which stretches from Anstruther in Scotland down to Whitby, to the Anglo-Scottish Fish Producers' Association at Berwick which works under the rules of the EEC and is partly funded by them. There are other similar groups imposing the regulations all round the British Isles. The quota figures were evolved from calculations made by scientific officers employed by the EEC.

The practical result for Whitby trawlers is that by the second week of a month they can have caught their allotted amount and cannot put to sea again until the start of the next month; skippers will tell you that it is impossible to go to sea and catch sufficient of other varieties of fish to cover their costs.

Jim Leadley has been involved in the political side of fishing for the past few years representing the industry in the EEC. He was also, until 1981, skipper of a trawler catching cod, and has been followed by his sons. He says that, whilst he has a high opinion of scientists, in all assessments of fish stocks they start off with an educated guess and from that they do calculations and they can get a long way out. The cod stocks certainly were running down but not to the extent that they calculated. "They were wrong and we've proved they were

wrong and I expect that very shortly the North Sea quota will go up by 30,000 or 40,000 tons.

"The prime consideration of the Whitby fleet has always been to catch cod and everything else was a bye-catch. Now they will need to diversify, to adapt their gear, to adapt their fishing to different species, whiting, haddock, turbot and plaice, varieties which they have been catching in with the cod but they have not really been looking for."

Mr Leadley says, "I must bring politics into it: quotas are not a conservation measure – they are not a catching restriction, they are a landing restriction. If we go fishing for other species and catch cod which we are not allowed to land – what do we do with it? Throw them back – but they will be dead; like every other variety except some flat fish, cod have swim bladders and once they come to the surface and the bladder is damaged they've had it. The problem is that the North Sea is a totally mixed fishing; if I go to catch haddock and whiting I will also catch cod and there's nothing I can do about it. What are we saving?

"You can modify your nets to make the mesh larger but the one fish that won't escape is the cod with its large blunt head – the whiting will go through because its head is like a torpedo, and so is the haddock but not the cod. The only compromise can be to enlarge the mesh to some extent, and certain fishing areas will have to be closed for some part of the year with no fishing at all."

The days of simply going fishing have gone. There is not just the bureaucracy laying down rules and quotas, there is also a policing of the boats which means that boats can be boarded almost every week. Each skipper must, as accurately as he can, enter in a log book details

The vigil on the West Pier extension when a boat was overdue; little different from those that waited for the return of the whaling fleet or watched helplessly from the cliffs as sailing ships were wrecked along the coast.

of his day's catch, its weight and variety to the satisfaction of the Naval Fishery Protection service patrolling the grounds and overseeing the EEC rules – although they do not actually check the weight of fish caught. There is also a North East Sea Fisheries patrol boat stationed at Whitby with authority to check boats inside the three mile limit (boats over ten metres long are barred) and to warn off from the two prohibited areas – one north of Whitby and the other near Filey – but with no power to check catches. There is also the Yorkshire Water Authority whose jurisdiction over the river

extends out to six miles but is not concerned with the keel boats which do not pick up the salmon and trout which is their concern. Mr Leadley says, "In all my years of trawling I have only caught three salmon, so I reckon they must commit suicide if they get in a trawl!" Part of the reason is that salmon and sea trout are not "shoaling" fish and individually they are capable of outstripping a trawler whilst she is dragging her net and they usually escape. Also, salmon and sea trout generally hug the coast when heading for their "home" rivers and are away from the normal trawling areas.

Above
"Crossing the Bar" at Whitby – was this whence came the title of the the well-known hymn?

Left
"Provider" crosses the Bar in July 1962 with an audience watching from the end of the West Pier, where cut-outs in the stonework date back to the Napoleonic Wars when they were used as gun embrasures.

There will always be dispute between those who fish inside the three-mile limit, mostly coblemen who like to think of it as their territory, and the keelboat men who generally fish much further out but are themselves restrained from working an area twelve miles and out to twenty miles where hundreds of larger beam-trawlers from several nations and from Lowestoft and Brixham work all the year round making it a no-go area for trawlers, so that the Whitby boats must either travel forty or fifty miles out – "and who wants to do that in winter with a hurricane forecast?" – or move nearer and into the three-mile area. The coblemen say that their shellfish catch has declined since the bigger boats started trawling inshore, the keelboat men say that they seldom catch crabs in the trawl but do take some lobsters. They also aver that whilst they can avoid trawling near crab pots because the markers are usually visible, they have a problem with nets which they are told are in one place, in good faith, but are actually in another. One must also suspect that another factor is the inbuilt tendency of fishermen to be very secretive where their favourite bit of ground is concerned!

The coblemen and boats of less than ten metres have one advantage in that they are not subject to quota and, as one said, "we would have a job to catch as many cod as the quota allows the bigger boats".

The prohibited areas where trawling is completely forbidden within the three mile limit are from Staithes Pier to Sandsend Ness and round Filey Brigg and were originally so designated because they were thought to be spawning and kindergarten areas for fish. Mr Clem James, chairman of the North East Sea Fisheries Committee, says: "I think its a nonsense but we think they have value in that cobles can work static gear without interference from trawlers. Trawlers can trawl legitimately within the three mile limit on every other part of the coast – after they obtain a permit (which is on demand) from the North Sea Fisheries Committee. The only ones barred are those over sixty feet long.

"There is no right to preserve the three mile limit for coblemen, and they do also fish outside that limit. So both trawlers and cobles are legitimately fishing the same ground and this is where the dispute arises. The two types of fishing are not compatible, and the only way out is compromise which is very difficult to achieve."

Mr James says: "Not all coblemen are angels – they put down pots and don't mark them properly. The trawlers who pick the pots up and are willing to pay compensation are told that every pot is brand new. There's a certain amount of legitimate grievance from each side. There's also the problem of telling the trawlermen where the pots are, and most of the cobles don't have electronics on board and simply say where it is by reference to shore marks, which can work very well if everyone knows the coastline. If a Staithes coble says my pots or nets are 'at Potash Chimney bearing so-and-so, and Old Nab bearing so-and-so' with any luck the trawler will know where they are, but as they move further north and the pots are supposed to be 'at Wesleyan Chapel bearing so-and-so and Smith's Farm bearing so-and-so', there's a lot of room for error.

"I must also say that of all the fleets we deal with – Bridlington, Scarborough, Shields – we get most complaints about the Whitby trawler men. I don't believe any of them would deliberately tow coblemens' gear away but there comes a time when they get careless or tired and go through. But unless we get co-operation we can't make it any better." However, the Whitby men contend that theirs is the most efficient inshore fleet and have the local knowledge to work inshore.

Mr James says: "There is a school of thought that says the three mile limit should be reserved for coblemen, but against that there is the fact that it would limit these small boats to that area, and conversely a trawler who came into that area and caught up pots would never admit it and pay compensation because he would be proving himself guilty of poaching."

Wry comment on the disputed ground came from a cobleman who, standing on the East Pier looking at a trawler working near the cliffs, said: "He's trawling for rabbits, not fish."

Another who used to work close inshore between Whitby and Sandsend was reputed to be trawling for golf balls which, it was alleged, he then sold back to the club whose golf course runs along the cliff top!

Some explanation must be made of the activities and jurisdiction of the North East Sea Fisheries Committee of which Mr Clem James has been chairman for over eight years. The Committee is one of a number covering the whole of the coastline, established by a government statute to regulate, maintain and preserve the fishery within the three miles limit. It has powers to make bye-laws which have to be ratified by the Ministry, to employ officers, operate patrol boats, to enforce bye-laws and National Conservation laws within the three miles limit. It has influence through consultations with the Ministry outside three miles and probably will eventually extend its cover to six miles or more.

Quotas are not the concern of the Committee, they do not inspect catches. They police the catching and landing of undersized fish, and lobsters, trawling in the prohibited areas off Filey and between Sandsend and Staithes, checking that trawlers inside three miles are under sixty feet long. They are involved in consultations whenever there is a pollution issue – when somebody wants to put an effluent into the water – with the Water Authorities, Yorkshire, Northumberland, Anglian and Trent. The North East area covers from Donna Nook in Lincolnshire to the Tyne.

Their patrol boat, the *North East Guardian*, built to the same specification as the Arran lifeboat, started work in 1986 and has been extremely successful. Mr James says, "We feel that we have helped to protect gear in the conflict between fixed and trawling gear; we have caught offenders – we thought our fishermen were too wise to be caught, but the patrol boat has caught eight offenders trawling in prohibited areas in this first year. The boat cost £360,000, there are three crew to pay, plus fuel and insurance and because the Committee and its activities are funded by those County Councils with seaboards in the area I don't think it is realistic to expect to have

more than one boat. Our next objective is to employ more crew so that the boat can spend more time at sea."

The Committee was established in 1866 but until 1945, when new methods of fishing came into being and trawling became the major activity, shore officers were sufficient. Up to then the fishing had all been potting and line fishing. There had been suggestions as far back as 1918 that a patrol boat was needed but the County Councils thought it too expensive.

Mr James says, "There must be a major increase in mesh size to get the increases we are looking for. The present size catches too many young fish which is not only bad for stocks but also does not make sense economically – leave that fish a year and its value increases because, firstly it increases in size and weighs more, and secondly it increases in value per stone so that a fish that weighs 1lb this year and 1½lbs next year has not only gone up fifty per cent in weight but it has probably gone up fifty per cent in value. The bigger fish could fetch £4 a stone instead of £2 and whilst the bringing in of a larger mesh size would mean smaller catches for a year, during which the economics would more than make up." True though that is, those same economics would surely include price increases for the consumer in a market where supply and demand rules the price.

The North Sea Fisheries Committee has been fighting for several yeas to bring in a minimum mesh size of 110mm which would have been a help but not the total answer. They contend that quotas are not the answer even in areas where it is possible to fish for just one particular species of fish because illegal practices would come in. The fact that a bigger fish has more value, as has been explained, could mean fishermen throwing back standard size fish – which would then be dead anyway – and fishing on to catch bigger ones whilst still totalling, say, the ten tons of cod their quota allows. "You haven't saved anything – they've killed more and thrown it overboard."

Mr James says, "I wanted to bring in the larger mesh sizes years ago but the fishermen's

The other fishing industry – Whitby is reputedly the largest centre in the country for party fishing and almost daily a fleet sets out, each boat carrying a dozen men with fishing rods for a day's "sport" which became almost an industry. After objections by professionals to the selling of catches on the harbourside that practice has been stopped. The picture shows one of the most successful party boat skippers, Alan Boocock, in June 1984 when his party caught 184 stone of prime cod.

representatives wouldn't have it at that time. Now they're being converted but they're too late – the situation is desperate. Its a coincidence that two years ago there must have been a good brood of cod and this has meant the coblemen have had a good winter with their lines but the trawlers have been taking small fish just the same. For the long term solution you must let more small fish escape".

An entirely separate matter is the industrial fishing. One authority is of the opinion that the Danish fleet uses only six boxes of fish, out of 200 caught, for human consumption, and the rest is for fertiliser factories, fish meal, etc. Mr James says, however, that they are fishing for species that are not wanted for human consumption, the pout and the blue whiting. "This has gone on legitimately for many years; our own herring were used for pet food and fish meal – and even ploughed into the land in the days of glut. With the present situation, their activities must be carefully monitored to see that they don't kill immature commercial species, whiting, cod, haddock and so on. They are allowed to use small mesh nets but there are places where there are heavy concentrations of pout and blue whiting. The by-catch of cod and whiting must be seen to be very low." Other commentators have stronger views, insisting that industrial fishing must be banned completely because not only are the smaller mesh nets killing immature fish but also the feed that other fish need – all fish are predators.

"But," says Clem James, "at the risk of being very unpopular I must stress that many English fishermen are not angels and will bend the rules when it suits them. The Scottish are even worse – I have castigated them over the last ten or fifteen years that they are a very rapacious fishing nation; they are very good fishermen, very efficient, but rapacious to the extent of defeating the concepts of conservation."

That conservation is helped by using larger mesh nets has been proved by the Norwegians – the only non-EEC country fishing in the North Sea. They increased their mesh size a few years ago and the stocks of cod in their area have increased dramatically, so much so that they have invited some British boats to fish there.

To return to the local situation in 1987, it would seem that there are two conflicting groups and since there is no way of limiting cobles to one area and trawlers to another, there is little likelihood of change. The imposition of quotas on the trawler fleet must exacerbate the situation. Anything that will help in any small way to prevent tempers rising can only be done by co-operation for to try and impose more regulations by yet another committee would be to increase an already top-heavy bureaucracy. Proper marking of gear, proper information passed to boats in the area, is something that the coblemen can do which would help. And the trawlers need to take note of what they are told is the position of fixed gear and be more careful. A coble can't afford the sophisticated electronics to tell exactly where his pots are – he doesn't earn enough to pay for the hundreds of thousands of pounds' worth that the trawlers have – but they will inevitably gradually get some, which will help.

The party fishing boats – and Whitby is the largest centre in the country with, generally, a completely different set of boats involved in taking out a dozen amateur sea anglers apiece for a day's fishing – are taking cod which is not recorded in the official records. From the keelboatmen's point of view this is probably regarded as a good thing and they don't want to know. But if the quota restrictions on cod really begin to bite, then must not those whose livelihood depends on it begin to look at these others who, even in a small way, are depleting the stocks? Mind you, I think the angler on the end of the pier will be left to his quiet contemplation.

8. Survival

Whitby is not unique as a fishing centre where the men have seen their traditional ways altered so radically that their industry seems in peril. There is the fate of the Humber industry, where competition between the markets on opposite side of the river plus the Icelandic no-go area killed a thriving port. We cannot catch enough fish for our consumption and some Icelandic fish is now coming in. The Icelanders, whilst it was normally wrong to go to war with us at that time, have in the event made a very good move for them and for the fish stocks. Whilst they stopped us catching fish in their area, they built up their own fleet with good conservation measures and they now have "tons of fish". The odd thing is that whilst it decimated our distant waters' fleet, it had the opposite effect on our inshore fleet; before the Icelandic war, the inshore fleet probably caught ten per cent of the fish that was eaten in this country, the distant water fleet caught eighty per cent and ten per cent was imported. With no fishing off Iceland, our inshore fleet has a much bigger market for its product.

The fishing industry has been a trade passed down through generations and sons have almost automatically learned from their fathers – and grandfathers. The great whaling days went because of diminishing uses for the oil and bone, long before conservation reared its head. What seemed endless shoals of herring were so depleted by hoovering up of the young fish as well as the mature by factory ships that now, after a period when none were allowed to be caught, local boats still cannot find amounts that are worth catching in the periods when it is allowed off this coast, never mind bring visions of the days when visiting Scottish fleets filled the harbour. The limitation on taking salmon and trout in the tidal waters of the river will not affect the legitimate fishermen working out at sea and may, it would seem, actually improve the prices they get because of a cutting down of the "black market" supply to restaurants and a gradual increase in the fish caught at sea because of more fish successfully reaching the breeding grounds. But it serves as another reminder that the balance of nature can be easily upset.

 The immediate problem which has caused quota restrictions to be placed on the amount of cod caught has been brought about by the same modern intensive working. The practical effects are still being worked through but already (mid 1987) the story is that the amounts allowed for boats over ten metres long are insufficient to cover the costs of crew and diesel fuel, that boats will have to tie up when their monthly quota has been reached. The regulations have been imposed by the EEC and in theory cover all the nations of the Community but it seems that some governments are less in control than is ours and local fishermen have serious doubts that continental boats are as stringent in keeping to their quotas. The hope must be that there is a relaxation in the amount allowed to be caught.

There is a great difference between these cod quotas and those imposed locally in the days of the herring glut – when market prices were used as a cut-off point and the surplus went for fertiliser and pet food. The cod quotas do now allow the catching of fish for any purpose which exceeds the limit.

Cobles and boats of less than ten metres seem less affected. They can make a living out their allowance and some have said they would

have a hard job to catch as many as their quota. The party fishing boats seem generally to exceed the 10 metres length and, one would think, would be treated as an unwanted complication.

Will it come to the point where an official stands on the quayside to police the regulations? Will Whitby – and other similar small fishing ports – have a smaller fleet? Will trawling inside the three-mile limit, traditionally the province of cobles, increase as the larger boats need to look for other fish to catch?

Mr Jim Leadley, of Whitby, who has been President and Chairman of the National Fishermen's Federation for six years until his retirement in May 1987, says: "I think Whitby will survive. It will have a short lean time but by the very fact that it is go-ahead, can adapt and has adapted I have no fears about the industry. It will survive an era of no-go areas at certain times of year and an increase in mesh sizes to help fish stocks. The quota will increase, there will be enough bread-and-butter fishing, haddock has always been popular and they will concentrate more on it, whiting, plaice, lemon soles are all there to be caught. They'll never fish the North Sea out, simply because it will become non-economic before it gets to that stage, and the North Sea is the most prolific breeding area in the world. Given half a chance the stocks will increase rapidly."

"A great deal of damage was done when the EEC was producing its Common Fisheries' policy; for political reasons they were giving member nations inflated allocations of "paper fish" which did not exist so that everyone thought they were getting a good share. The present quotas are an attempt to get back to sensible amounts from the levels which were handed out – and were never there. The present ideas are, to any practical fisherman,

Both photographs are of the Dock End at Whitby, with some 80 years between. The older one, by F. M. Sutcliffe, was taken in the era of oars and sails, the other shows motor power and echo-sounders. The buildings on the left tell a story; the old one has warehouses fronting on to a wooden quay littered with barrels. The modern photograph shows New Quay road, a thoroughfare for motor traffic, and with wide pavements, seats and flower beds. Whitby is still a working port but acknowledges the demands of tourism. The Parish Church and Abbey ruins on the east cliff remain the same, but are thronged with visitors who are the mainstay of the finances. With the restrictions on fishing, could it be that the trawlers will be taking trips round the bay?

totally wrong, for what sense is there in being put in a position where you catch fish you are trying not to catch and have no option but to throw it back because you can't bring it in. You throw it back but its already dead. Where's the conservation in that?

"We are dealing with civil servants and politicians, and the last thing they think of is the practicality. We have seen what they have achieved with the Common Agricultural Policy – a mess. They have handed out subsidies and the result is stock piles. The opposite happens with the Fishing Policy; they hand out no grants except for building more boats, and that at a time when there are too many boats. A three years' moratorium on new boats, except as replacement for old or damaged craft is something I have been suggesting, with the grants saved to be used to assist the remaining fishermen who comply with the need for larger mesh nets and restricted areas, so helping them out over the lean three years which I feel would be all that is necessary to build stocks up.

"The restrictions are now being enforced all round the North Sea; the Continentals, and the Norwegians who, whilst not in the EEC, are allowed to fish there, are having to comply. The Russians and the Eastern block countries are not allowed to fish in the North Sea, one of the few good things which came out of the EEC regulations, but their factory ships take much of the Scottish herring and mackerel catches – which is the main outlet for them. The trade is very strictly controlled with a British inspector on board to check how much fish is being transferred and the prices given."

The strange thing is that there is a shortage of fish landed in this country; there is an exceptional demand caused by health experts and doctors who stress the benefits of eating more fish – they can quote the Eskimos whose diet is high in fish and in fish-feeding sea-mammals and they rarely suffer from coronary or circulatory diseases. There's no need to advertise. The price has to be right to compete with other foods and it is. The quality of fish has vastly improved since the demise of the Distant Waters' fleet where what they caught off Iceland was at least a week and often a fortnight old. The quality of fish landed on Whitby market is very good. There are four excellent processing factories and fast transport takes the product all over the country. The problem that may arise for Whitby from the quota is the amount of fish available.

What is not in any doubt is the Whitby fishermen's confidence in their product, and I quote one chauvinistic opinion – "Whitby Fish has a name second to none throughout the country, and, like Scotch Beer, there could be supplies labelled as 'Whitby Fish' which never saw the port."

Opposite, top
Inside the wheelhouse of a modern Whitby trawler showing some of the electronic aids – there are more behind the skipper as he stands at the wheel, and one wonders how soon the wheel will be replaced by switches?

Opposite, bottom
Three of Whitby's modern fleet with their masthead arrays of aerials and direction finders.

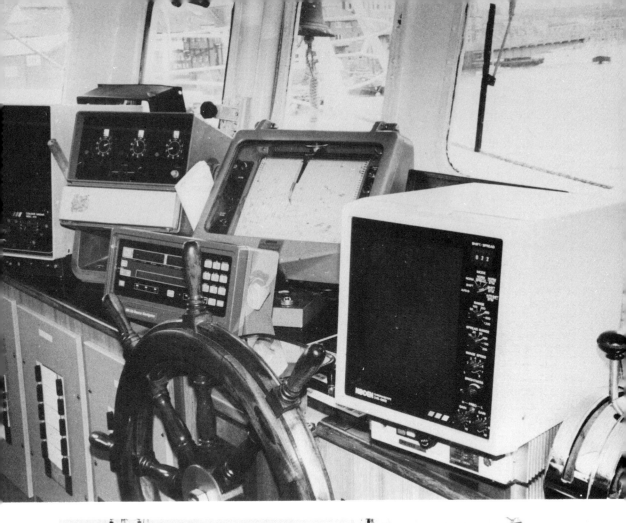

Above

The upper harbour photographed from the new high level bridge, an area which in the 1700s was encircled by yards and dry docks. The slipway in the foreground is at Whitehall Shipyard where it is hoped the replica "Endeavour" will be built.

Opposite

Another view of the modern upper harbour with its yachting marina and Endeavour Wharf for cargo shipping. The car park is where Thomas Fishburn had his yard – here Captain James Cook's ships were built in the 1770s.

Days of plenty – prime fish laid out in Easter week 1954.